Ruwantissa Abeyratne

Aviation and Climate Change

In Search of a Global Market Based Measure

 Springer

Ruwantissa Abeyratne
Global Aviation Consultancies Inc.
Cote Saint Luc, QC
Canada

ISSN 2192-855X   ISSN 2192-8568   (electronic)
ISBN 978-3-319-08442-8   ISBN 978-3-319-08443-5   (eBook)
DOI 10.1007/978-3-319-08443-5

Library of Congress Control Number: 2014943406

Springer Cham Heidelberg New York Dordrecht London

Printed on acid-free paper

Springer is part of Springer Science+Business Media (www.springer.com)

Preface

The Stern Review of October 2006 titled *The Economics of Climate Change* stated that if no action is taken to reduce emissions, the concentration of greenhouse gases in the atmosphere could reach double its preindustrial level as early as 2035, virtually committing us to a global average temperature rise of over 2 degrees centigrade. The David Suzuki Foundation, in its official website says that "for a relatively small industry, aviation has a disproportionately large impact on the climate system. It presently accounts for 4–9 % of the total climate change impact of human activity." A Report published by the Federation of American Scientists for the Congressional Research Service in 2010, has stated that aircraft are a significant source of greenhouse gases—compounds that trap the sun's heat, with effects on the Earth's climate. In the United States, aircraft of all kinds are estimated to emit between 2.6 % and 3.4 % of the nation's total greenhouse gas (GHG) emissions, "depending on whether one counts international air travel." A Report titled "Predict and Decide," published in 2006 by the Environmental Change Institute, University of Oxford said: "There is increasing recognition that aviation is a cause for concern in terms of its impact on climate. Yet, due to political difficulties in agreeing responsibilities, the emissions from international aviation (together with international shipping) were excluded from the Kyoto Protocol, and all related assessments. There is also a lack of clarity about how 'bad' aviation is."

As the specialized agency of the United Nations addressing issues of international civil aviation, the International Civil Aviation Organization (ICAO) was very active in the year 2013. With all its achievements of events planned and convened, meetings held, and assistance rendered to States, ICAO's greatest challenge was to prepare for the 38th Session of the Assembly of its 191 membership a credible and plausible framework for market based measures (MBMs) that could be applicable to aircraft engine emissions. Whether or not ICAO acquitted itself in this regard with credit at the Assembly session held from 24 September to 4 October 2013, only time and history will tell.

At the end of the Assembly session, ICAO issued a statement saying: "ICAO's States agreed to report back in 2016 with a proposal for a global MBM scheme capable of being implemented by 2020. Major efforts will need to be undertaken in order to address the challenges and accommodate specific concerns of developing States going forward."

There is no doubt that ICAO's role is daunting, as acknowledged by ICAO. It has to balance several interests, both of developed States and developing States in shaping the proposal. The Assembly resolved that the proposal should be developed within the parameters of work carried out by States and relevant Organizations through ICAO to achieve a global annual average fuel efficiency improvement efficiency of 2 % until 2020 and an aspirational global fuel efficiency improvement rate of 2 % per annum from 2021 to 2050, calculated on the basis of volume of fuel used per revenue ton kilometer performed.

If, as the Resolution requires, States and international organizations have to work through ICAO on this task, it is clear that what is required of ICAO over the triennium 2014–2016 is leadership and governance. The technical requirements aside, which the key players would be amply capable of handling, ICAO would have to move with a strong sense of purpose, direction, and conviction.

As an initial measure, ICAO will have to dispel current accusations from several sources regarding its own ineptitude in handling the subject. One commentator was loathe to comment at the end of the Assembly session that ICAO has been talking about dealing with carbon pollution from airplanes for 16 years, but doing nothing. He went on to say that ICAO should not be allowed to just keep playing its old game of promising climate action—next time—and then failing to deliver, voicing his concern that climate change was costing the aviation industry billions of dollars in canceled flights from extreme weather, and hurting the whole planet.

Some others have commented that ICAO's record in dealing with this subject reeks of the Organization's own feckless insouciance and lack of awareness of the magnitude of the problem. ICAO's vulnerability to attack is borne out by the fact that history is against the Organization. At its 21st Assembly (Montreal, 21st September–15 October 1974) ICAO was both ambivalent on and resistant to fuel efficiency standards for new aircraft and in 2004, rejected a global emissions trading system. If a global MBM would have been made applicable in 2012, aviation's contribution to global warming could have been reduced by 31 %. Instead, pushing it all back to 2020 is just plain lethargy and incompetence. Popular comment on the 38th Session of the Assembly was that: no concrete action was taken at the Montreal Assembly. Delegates merely authorized ICAO to develop a global MBM mechanism over the next 3 years. (According to an ICAO spokesperson, the details "will be determined over the course of the coming triennium, based on discussions amongst our member states,"); even if the next ICAO assembly adopts the plan in 2016, it won't take effect until 2020; and, until then, the sector's emissions will continue to rise, as increases in passenger volume offset incremental improvements in fuel efficiency.

As a first measure, the leadership of ICAO should restore the relevancy and credibility of the Organization by establishing time lines and a work program for the next 3 years that would ensure ICAO's delivery to the 39th session of the

Assembly an MBM scheme that is workable and applicable in 2020. An Agenda for work was presented to the Council in early 2014, after the 38th Session of the Assembly closed. It was too little, too late. To an extent, this was the current approach adopted by the ICAO Council (which has been a practice for many decades) of establishing and adopting a work program for each session of the Council and muddling through its overall responsibility in this instance simply will not work, as was proven in the last triennium. The 3-year work program should not be couched in ambivalent terms and ambiguous text which does not give either the Council or the Secretariat purpose and direction. Secondly, ICAO should approach its work in a structured manner by gaining insight and comprehension of what is really required to appease both the developed and developing States.

There are several considerations in the development of an international agreement relating to an MBM scheme. One is to cap emissions at existing rates with a freeze and impose a percentage reduction. Developed States would be at an advantage in this situation. However, if reductions are based on per capita basis States such as China and India would be at an advantage with their large populations because of their low emissions rate per person. This formula could only change if there are dramatic increases in emissions rates in China and India which will be the case in 10–20 years to come. From an equitable perspective, the per capita principle is intuitive and scores high, on the basis that, as against allocations based on a national status quo, a person living in China should not be given emission rights which are just a small fraction of the rights given to a person living in the United States.

A suggested approach towards regulating greenhouse gas emissions is a tax based on units consumed. For instance, if an entity consumes each unit which produces a social cost of X, the tax per unit would be X, which would ensure that the unit of energy is used provided the private benefit exceeds the unit cost. Therefore a government permit, issued to consume a unit would carry a price tag of X, allowing the entity to trade the unit at X as well. The advantage in this private permit approach would be twofold. On the one hand it would generate revenue and, on the other, it would deter arbitrary and wayward emissions. However, if such a method is applied to aircraft emissions, the revenue earned would have to be considered a charge and not a tax in accordance with existing ICAO policies and pumped back into the development of air transport, for instance for research and development on the manufacture of more efficient and less gas-emitting aircraft engines. Against this wide ranging backdrop of distributive justice, international paretianism would have special significance in a treaty or agreement on an MBM scheme in that such a scheme must ensure that it is designed to ensure that all States could consider themselves better off than they were before.

Any MBM scheme that ICAO comes up with will have to promote compliance through clear measures. Above all, the proposed scheme would have to introduce a process of legalization which incorporates its principles into the legal system of a participating State. The rules would have to be precise and offer a fair deal to every State concerned. The Parties themselves would have to agree on authentic interpretations of the provisions of the scheme. This has been done before. Since 1979, the Convention on Long-range Trans-boundary Air pollution (LRTAP) which has addressed some of the major environmental problems of the United Nations Environmental Programme region through scientific collaboration and policy negotiation, and which has been extended by eight Protocols that identify specific measures to be taken by Parties to cut their emissions of air pollutants, has adopted "common understandings" to define specific terminology of the Sulphur Protocol of 1985. In the 1983 International Undertaking on Plant Genetic Resources, The Food and Agriculture Organization—a specialized agency of the United Nations the same as ICAO, has done the same thing to clarify and establish universally acceptable interpretations.

Any instrument involving a global market based measure under the aegis of ICAO would inevitably and essentially be one that would be developed under international law and within the United Nations system, whether by treaty, resolution, declaration, or Standard. Therefore, this book will contain an introductory chapter on the development of international law, treaty structure, and the United Nations System.

The lawmaking process of the scheme and its negotiation must involve the effective participation of key States. Through effective participation, States will ensure compliance and implementation and commitment to the goals of the scheme. It goes without saying that such a scheme should contain clear and stringent provisions for violations. Polarization, as was seen in the significant opposition to the European Emissions Trading Scheme by emerging economies and economic giants such as the United States and China would only continue to stultify the process. The end result of such a scenario would be individual legis-lation—a decided failure of ICAO.

Ruwantissa Abeyratne

Contents

Chapter 1
Introduction

Introduction

Both The United Nations and its predecessor *The League of Nations* came into being as responses by the international community of States[1] to war and destruction and the former stands for unity among States on the basic principle that that the nations[2] of the world are united under the rule of law. This club of States called The United Nations are bound by a fundamental treaty—called the *Charter of the United Nations*—which sets universal principles of conduct driven by the principles of international law. Much of the rule of law[3]—under the aegis of the United Nations—is enunciated through international treaties, whether they relate to genocide or civil aviation or any other subject of international concern.

Therefore, at the heart of the United Nations mandate is promoting the rule of law at the national and international levels. The United Nations attempts to resolve national and international conflict by establishing respect for the rule of law, with a

---

[1] A State is identified by four different characteristics in the *Montevideo Convention on the Rights and Duties of States* of 1933, Article 1 of which states: The state as a person of international law should possess the following qualifications: (a) a permanent population; (b) a defined territory; (c) government; and (d) capacity to enter into relations with the other states.

[2] A nation represents the people of a State. The United Nations Charter refers to nations, or people of the world and therefore implicitly charging the United Nations to unite the entire world.

[3] For the United Nations, the rule of law refers to a principle of governance in which all persons, institutions and entities, public and private, including the State itself, are accountable to laws that are publicly promulgated, equally enforced and independently adjudicated, and which are consistent with international human rights norms and standards. It requires, as well, measures to ensure adherence to the principles of supremacy of law, equality before the law, accountability to the law, fairness in the application of the law, separation of powers, participation in decision-making, legal certainty, avoidance of arbitrariness and procedural and legal transparency. S/2004/ 616, *Report of the Secretary-General on the Rule of Law and Transitional Justice in Conflict and Post-Conflict Societies.*

© The Author(s) 2014
R. Abeyratne, *Aviation and Climate Change*, SpringerBriefs in Law,
DOI: 10.1007/978-3-319-08443-5_1

view to achieving a durable peace both during and in the aftermath of conflict, which in turn is geared to protecting human rights and sustaining economic progress and development. The main driver of the United Nations is the adherence of States to treaties and the resolutions that are passed by the United Nations system, whether they be adopted in the General Assembly or the Security Council or a specialized agency of the United Nations. The principle of the rule of law embedded in the Charter of the United Nations contains and embodies elements applicable to the conduct of relations between States. The main United Nations organs, including the General Assembly and the Security Council, have compelling roles in this regard, which are derived from and require action in accordance with the provisions of the Charter.

The United Nations Charter, which is applicable to the world as a whole encompasses people of all of its 193 member States, and is therefore a universal document which arguably cannot be fettered by arbitrary claims of State sovereignty when it comes to determining the rights of people, wherever they might be. Although sovereignty of States has been defined as:

> The relations between States signifies independence. Independence in relation to a portion of the globe is the right to exercise therein, to the exclusion of any other State, the function of a State. The development of the national organization of States during the last few centuries and, as a corollary, the development of international law, have established this principle of exclusive competence of the State in regard to its own territory in such a way as to make it the point of departure in settling most questions that concern international relations. Sovereignty in relation to a portion of the surface of the globe is the legal condition necessary for the inclusion of such portion in the territory of any particular State[4]

In the modern context, sovereignty should not be viewed as an absolute right that can be applied by a State at will. Current international trends, demarcations of rights and duties and the sharing of responsibility by States ascribe to the community of nations a certain right to be unobtrusively involved in and comment upon the welfare of people across the globe. One may attribute this trend to globalization; the lifting of trade barriers or simply the mass migration from State to State which occurred prolifically over the past 4 decades.

United Nations Secretary General Kofi Annan, in defining sovereignty said:

> State sovereignty is being redefined by the forces of globalization and international cooperation. The state is now widely understood to be the servant of its people, not vice versa. At the same time, individual sovereignty—the human rights and fundamental freedoms of each and every individual as enshrined in our Charter—has been enhanced by a renewed consciousness of the right of every individual to control his or her own destiny.[5]

---

[4] Per Justice Huber in *The Island of Palmas Case*. See 2RIAA, at pp. 829, at 838 (1928).

[5] *The Economist*, September 16, 1999 at 21.

Much of what goes on in the world, be it in Kiev (Ukraine) or Cairo (Egypt) or for that matter in Syria or Thailand clearly indicates that individuals control their own destiny and are entitled to live their lives without persecution, segregation, discrimination and with dignity.

This brings to bear the need to address the claim by many States that the United Nations cannot intervene in the internal affairs of a State. Admittedly, in essence this claim is valid and should legally obviate any interference from any State or the United Nations, as stated in Article 2.7 of the United Nations Charter—that nothing contained in the Charter shall authorize the United Nations to intervene in matters which are essentially within the domestic jurisdiction of any State. However, the international community has intervened where necessary to protect the interests of people irrespective of ostensible sovereignty, as in the case of the imposition of the no-fly zone in Libya by Resolution 1973 of 2011, adopted by the Security Council, which stated *inter alia* that member States that have notified the Secretary-General, acting nationally or through regional organizations or arrangements, and acting in cooperation with the Secretary-General, were authorized to take all necessary measures, to protect civilians and civilian populated areas under threat of attack in the Libyan Arab Jamahiriya, including Benghazi, while excluding a foreign occupation force of any form on any part of Libyan territory, and requested the Member States concerned to inform the Secretary-General immediately of the measures they take pursuant to the authorization conferred by the Resolution which was required to be immediately reported to the Security Council. The Resolution also authorized member States that have notified the Secretary-General and the Secretary-General of the League of Arab States, acting nationally or through regional organizations or arrangements, to take all necessary measures to enforce compliance with the ban on flights imposed, as necessary, and requested the States concerned in cooperation with the League of Arab States to coordinate closely with the Secretary General on the measures they were taking to implement this ban, including by establishing an appropriate mechanism for implementing the relevant provisions of the Resolution.

This Chapter will discuss the evolution of international law and the law of treaties, which are the fundamental bases of the United Nations and the manner in which the United Nations, through its main organs, has conducted itself within its scope as the global entity that develops international law.

Evolution of International Law

The genesis of international law may well lie in the seminal European Charter—the Peace of Westphalia—which was signed in 1648. This document recognized unrestrained sovereignty of states and effectively consolidated the concept of world unity through sovereign states.

The next significant step was the Concert of Europe—a haphazard system of consultation between the great countries of Europe—which was established by the

Settlement of Vienna in 1815 and followed by the Congress of Aix-la-Chapelle in 1818. The Concert emerged as a corollary to the Napoleonic Wars and provided a forum which maintained and balanced power between the European nations for a century. One of the salient features of the Concert was that although the treaty admitted of consultation and conference on the devolution of power among states, its findings or decisions had no obligatory effect on the Great Powers. This perceived inadequacy of the Concert resulted in its impotence and inability to impose adherence by states of its findings or decisions and is often attributed to states having a free hand in doing as they pleased to each other in World War I.

As history would demonstrate time and time again, the aftermath of a major disaster brings fresh thinking for reformation and revival. After World War I, states adopted the Paris Settlement of 1919, partially as atonement for the bankruptcy and inability of the Concert to ensure uniformity in international accord and also to infuse new ideas and rules of conduct for the international community. The Paris Settlement, which retained for the most part the spirit of the Peace of Westphalia, set the tone for the establishment of the League of Nations which further strengthened the bonds of unity between states, based on the wartime collaboration between Associated and Allied Powers. The League of Nations adopted the principle that undertakings of international law would actively determine conduct among governments, without abdicating *jus ad bellum,* or the right of war. This in turn resulted in failure, as was seen in 1939, when, without reference to the League of Nations, Britain and France hastened to come to Poland's assistance when it was attacked by Germany.

At this stage in history, international law was considered as simply law binding upon States in their relations with each other. The Provisional International Court of Justice (the predecessor to the International Court of Justice) decided in the famous *Lotus* case of 1927:

> International law governs relations between independent States. The rules of law binding upon States therefore emanate from their own free will as expressed in conventions or by usages generally accepted as expressing principles of law and established in order to regulate the relations between those co-existing independent communities or with a view to the achievement of common aims. Restrictions upon the independence of States cannot therefore be presumed.[6]

The aftermath of World War II saw the advent of the United Nations and the United Nations Charter, the latter of which proclaims that the United Nations is based on the sovereign equality of all members. The Charter also provides that less powerful nations recognize the pre-eminence of the Great Powers as guardians of international peace and security.[7] With the exception of this predominant innovation

---

[6] PCIJ (1927) Ser. A, No 9 at 18.

[7] Article 24 of the United Nations Charter provides that In order to ensure prompt and effective action by the United Nations, its Members confer on the Security Council primary responsibility for the maintenance of international peace and security, and agree that in carrying out its duties under this responsibility the Security Council acts on their behalf. In discharging these duties the Security Council shall act in accordance with the Purposes and Principles of the United Nations.

of post-World War II accord, the rest of the Charter seems complacently to accord with the basic framework of international law which existed under the Peace of Westphalia. Judicial recognition of the United Nations as a subject of international law was given by the International Court of Justice (ICJ) in 1949, in the *Reparation for Injuries Case*,[8] where the ICJ pronounced the end of the old orthodoxy that states are the only subjects of international law, and advised that the United Nations, though not a state, had the capacity to bring certain kinds of claims directly against a state under the rubric of international law.

The many contributions of the United Nations to the development of international law have been both significant and sustained, ever since the United Nations General Assembly convened its first session in 1946. The General Assembly has been prolific in adopting numerous resolutions., declarations and conventions through diplomatic conferences. Guided by Article 13 of the United Nations Charter which places an obligation on the General Assembly to initiate studies and make recommendations for encouraging the progressive development of international law and its codification,[9] the Assembly, in November 1947, established the International Law Commission whose members were entrusted with the formulation of principles of international law. One of the first tasks of the Commission was to write a Draft Code of Offenses (sic) against Peace and Security of Mankind, which the Commission completed in 1954. The Draft Code provided that any act of aggression, including the employment by the authorities of a state of armed forces against another State for any purpose other than national or collective self-defense or in pursuance of a decision or recommendation of a competent organ of the United Nations, was an offence against the peace and security of mankind. The

---

(Footnote 7 continued)

The specific powers granted to the Security Council for the discharge of these duties are laid down in Chaps. 6, 7, 8, and 12. Article 24 also states that the Security Council shall submit annual and, when necessary, special reports to the General Assembly for its consideration Article 23 of the Charter provides that the Security Council shall consist of 15 Members of the United Nations. The Republic of China, France, the Union of Soviet Socialist Republics, the United Kingdom of Great Britain and Northern Ireland, and the United States of America shall be permanent members of the Security Council. The General Assembly shall elect ten other Members of the United Nations to be non-permanent members of the Security Council, due regard being specially paid, in the first instance to the contribution of Members of the United Nations to the maintenance of international peace and security and to the other purposes of the Organization, and also to equitable geographical distribution. Article 23 goes on to say that the non-permanent members of the Security Council shall be elected for a term of 2 years. In the first election of the non-permanent members after the increase of the membership of the Security Council from 11 to 15, two of the four additional members shall be chosen for a term of 1 year. A retiring member shall not be eligible for immediate re-election. Each member of the Security Council shall have one representative.

[8] *ICJ Report* (1949) 174.

[9] See *Charter of the United Nations and Statute of the International Court of Justice*, United Nations: New York, Article 13.1.a.

code also stipulated that any threat by the authorities of a state to resort to an act of aggression against another state was a similar offence.[10]

The sense of international responsibility that the United Nations ascribed to itself had reached a heady stage at this point, where the role of international law in international human conduct was perceived to be primary and above the authority of states. In its Report to the General Assembly, the International Law Commission recommended a draft provision which required:

> Every State has the duty to conduct its relations with other States in accordance with international law and with the principle that the sovereignty of each State is subject to the supremacy of international law.[11]

This principle, which forms a cornerstone of international conduct by states, provides the basis for strengthening international comity and regulating the conduct of states both internally—within their territories—and externally, towards other states. States are effectively precluded by this principle of pursuing their own interests untrammeled and with disregard to principles established by international law.

Development of International Law Through Treaties

A treaty, according Article 38(1) to the United Nations Charter is one of the sources of international law, the others being international custom, as evidence of a general practice accepted as law; the general principles of law recognized by civilized nations; and judicial decisions and the teachings of the most highly qualified publicists of the various nations, as subsidiary means for the determination of rules of law.

Treaties, conventions, agreements, protocols, exchanges of notes and other synonyms all mean one and the same thing at international law—that they are international transactions of a legal character. Treaties are concluded between states in written form and governed by international law, whether embodied in a single instrument or in two or more related instruments and whatever its particular designation.[12] Each treaty has four constituent elements: the capacity of the parties thereto to conclude agreement of the provisions of the treaty under international law; the intention of the parties to apply principles of international law when concluding agreement under a treaty; *consensus ad idem* or a meeting of the minds

---

[10] Article 2 of the Draft Code at 64–65.

[11] *Report of the International Law Commission to the General Assembly on the work of the First Session*, (1949) A/CN.4/13. June 9 at 21.

[12] *Vienna Convention on the Law of Treaties*, 1969, Done at Vienna on 23c May 1969, United Nations General Assembly Document *A/CONF.39/27*, 23 May 1969, Article 2(a). The Convention entered into force on 27 January 1980. UNTS Vol. 1155, p. 331.

of the parties[13]; and, the parties must have the intention to create legal obligations among themselves. These four elements form a composite regulatory process whereby a treaty becomes strong enough at international law to enable parties to settle their differences within the parameters of the treaty, make inroads into customary international law if necessary, and, transform an unorganized international community into one which may be organized under a uniform set of rules. Treaties are based on three fundamental principles of international law: good faith; consent; and, international responsibility (Schwarzenberger and Brown 1976). Since international customary law does not prescribe any particular form for consensual agreements and requirements that would make them binding, the parties to a treaty could agree upon the form of treaty they intend entering into and make it binding among them accordingly. Legal bonds are established between nations because they wish to create them and, as is seen in the Preamble to the Chicago Convention, a statement to this effect is reflected in the treaty itself.[14] The main feature of a multilateral international agreement is that absolute rights that may have existed within states before the entry into force of such treaty would be transformed into relative rights in the course of a balancing process in which considerations of good faith and reasonableness play a prominent part. However, treaty provisions must be so written and construed as best to conform to accepted principles of international customary law (Greig 1976).

Great reliance is placed on treaties as a source of international law. The international Court of Justice, whose function it is to adjudicate upon disputes of an international character between states, applies as a source of law, international conventions which establish rules that are expressly recognized by the states

---

[13] There are instances where States may record their reservation on particular provisions of a convention while signing the document as a whole. The International Court of Justice in its examination of the Genocide Convention has ruled:

> The object and purpose of the Convention…limit both the freedom of making reservations and that of objecting to them. It follows that it is the compatibility of a reservation with the object and purpose of the Convention that must furnish the criterion for the attitude of a State in objecting to the reservation. 1 *I.C.J. Rep.* (1951) at 15.

[14] The Preamble to the Convention on International Civil Aviation, signed at Chicago on 7 December 1944 (ICAO Doc 7300/8: 2006) states:

> the undersigned governments having agreed on certain principles and arrangements in order that international civil aviation may be developed in a safe and orderly manner and that international air transport services may be established on the basis of equality of opportunity and operated soundly and economically; have accordingly concluded this Convention to that end.

involved in a dispute.[15] The Court also has jurisdiction to interpret a treaty at the request of a state.[16]

The *Vienna Convention on the Law of Treaties*[17] while recognizing treaties as a source of law, accepts free consent, good faith and the *pacta sunt servanda* as universally recognized elements of a treaty.[18] Article 11 of the Vienna Convention provides that the consent of a State to be bound by a treaty may be expressed by signature, exchange of instruments constituting a treaty, ratification, acceptance, approval or accession, or by any other means agreed upon. 'Ratification', 'acceptance', 'approval', and 'accession' generally mean the same thing, that is, that in each case the international act so named indicates that the State performing such act is establishing on the international plane its consent to be bound by a treaty. A State demonstrates its adherence to a treaty by means of the *pacta sunt servanda*, which is reflected in Article 26 of the Vienna Convention—that every treaty in force is binding upon the parties and must be performed by them in good faith. The validity of a treaty or of the consent of a State to be bound by a treaty may be impeached only through the application of the Vienna Convention[19] which generally requires that a treaty could be derogated upon only in circumstances the treaty in question so specifies[20]; a later treaty abrogates the treaty in question;[21] there is a breach of the treaty[22]; a *novus actus interveniens* or supervening act which makes the performance of the treaty impossible;[23]and the invocation by a State of the *Clausula Rebus Sic Stantibus*[24] wherein a fundamental change of circumstances (when such circumstances constituted an essential basis of the consent of the parties to be bound by the treaty) which has occurred with regard to those existing at the time of the conclusion of the treaty, and which was not foreseen by the parties, radically changes or transforms the extent of obligations of a State. A State may not invoke the fact that its consent to be bound by a treaty has been expressed in violation of a provision of its internal law regarding competence to conclude treaties and seek to invalidate its consent unless such violation was manifest and concerned a rule of its internal law of fundamental importance (Reuter 1989).

States or international organizations which are parties to such treaties have to apply the treaties they have signed and therefore have to interpret them. Although

---

[15] Statute of the International Court of Justice, *Charter of the United Nations and Statute of the International Court of Justice*, United Nations: New Y, Article 38.1 (a). See the discussion on the International Court of Justice that follows in the text related to note 42 *infra*.

[16] *Id.*, Article 36.2 (a).

[17] Vienna Convention, *supra*, note 12 at Preamble.

[18] *Id.*, Article 42.1.

[19] *Id.*, Article 57.

[20] *Id.*, Article 59.

[21] *Id.*, Article 60.

[22] *Id.*, Article 61.

[23] *Id.*, Article 62.

[24] *Id.*, Article 46.

the conclusion of a treaty is generally governed by international customary law to accord with accepted rules and practices of national constitutional law of the signatory States, the application of treaties are governed by principles of international law. If, however, the application or performance of a requirement in an international treaty poses problems to a state, the constitutional law of that state would be applied by courts of that State to settle the problem. Although Article 27 of the Vienna Convention requires States not to invoke provisions of their internal laws as justification for failure to comply with the provisions of a treaty, States are free to choose the means of implementation they see fit according to their traditions and political organization (von der Dunk 2014). The overriding rule is that treaties are juristic acts and have to be performed.

Every international treaty is affected by the fundamental dichotomy where, on the one hand, the question arises whether provisions of a treaty are enforceable at law, and, on the other, whether the principles of State sovereignty, which is *jus cogens* or mandatory law, would pre-empt the provisions of a treaty from being considered by states as enforceable. Article 53 of the Vienna Convention addresses this question and provides that, where treaties, which at the time of their conclusion conflict with a peremptory norm of general international law or *jus cogens* are void. A peremptory norm of general international law is a norm accepted and recognized by the international community of States as a whole as a norm from which no derogation is permitted and which can be modified only by a subsequent norm of general international law having the same character. The use of the words "as a whole" in article 53 effectively precludes individual States from considering on a subjective basis, particular norms as acceptable to the international community. The Vienna Convention has, by this provision, implicitly ensured the legal legitimacy of international treaties, and established the principle that treaties are in fact *jus cogens* and are therefore instruments containing provisions, the compliance with which is mandatory.

Modern Treaty Law

A treaty is an international agreement concluded between States[25] in written form and governed by international law, whether embodied in a single instrument or in two or more related instruments and whatever its particular designation.[26] The above notwithstanding, a treaty can be concluded between a State and another subject of international law such as an international Organization. An example is the Headquarters Agreement between ICAO and the Government of Canada.[27]

---

[25] A State has been defined in this Chapter. See *supra*, note 2.

[26] *Vienna Convention on the Law of Treaties*, Supra note 12, Article 2(a).

[27] Headquarters Agreement between Canada and ICAO of 14 April 1951, which paraphrased the 1947 Convention on the Privileges and Immunities of the Specialized Agencies. On 20 February 1992, the 1951 Agreement was terminated and superseded by a new Agreement that entered into force the same day. A new Supplementary Agreement was signed on 28 May 1999 superseding

When a State places its signature on a treaty it merely means that the State has agreed to the text in the instrument. It comes into effect for that State when it is ratified[28] by the State. At the time of ratification a State can record a reservation to a part of the treaty.[29]

It must be noted that a State can sign a treaty in two ways. The first is called attestation by "simple signature" which corresponds to the above statement—that such a signature merely denotes that a State agrees with the text of an instrument and a simple signature is subject to ratification, acceptance or approval. However, if a State attaches to the instrument what is called a "definitive signature" it means that the State has agreed to be bound by the treaty. Therefore a definitive signature obviates the need for that State to later ratify the treaty, as it has the same force as ratification.

The process of ratification usually goes through two phases. The first is the internal procedure where the State concerned has to attend to its constitutional provisions by sending the text of the instrument it has signed through its national legislature or parliament. Once parliament adopts the text as its internal law, the State then has to proceed with its international procedure of depositing its notice of ratification with the depository. In formal terminology this process is called the doctrine of incorporation where customary international law as incorporated in a treaty that has been signed by a State is recognized as the internal law of the land on the common law practice based on a presumption that the legislature does not intend to commit a breach of international law.[30]

As the Vienna Convention[31] provides, a treaty need not be signed. According to Article 12 of the Convention the consent of a State to be bound by a treaty is expressed by the signature of the representative of that State only in certain

---

(Footnote 27 continued)

the Supplementary Agreement signed in 1980 in order to reflect the relocation of the Organization's Headquarters to a new location on 999 University Street on November 1, 1996. See Supplementary Agreement Between the International Civil Aviation Organization and the Government of Canada Regarding the Headquarters of the International Civil Aviation Organization, Doc 9591.

[28] "Ratification", "acceptance", "approval" and "accession" mean in each case the international act so named whereby a State establishes on the international plane its consent to be bound by a treaty. See Vienna Convention , *supra*, note 6 at Article 2(b).

[29] "Reservation" means a unilateral statement, however phrased or named, made by a State, when signing, ratifying, accepting, approving or acceding to a treaty, whereby it purports to exclude or to modify the legal effect of certain provisions of the treaty in their application to that State. Id. 2(d).

[30] See *West Rand Central Gold Mining Company* v. *R.* [1905] 2. K.B. 391 per Lord Alverstone who stated in his judgment: "whatever has received the common consent of civilized nations must have received the assent of our country, and that to which we assented along with other nations in general may properly be called international law: and as such will be acknowledged and applied by our municipal tribunals to decide questions to which doctrines of international law may be relevant". *Id.* 397.

[31] *Supra,* note 12.

circumstances.[32] Article 13 goes on to say that the consent of States to be bound by a treaty constituted by instruments exchanged between them is expressed by that exchange when: the instruments provide that their exchange shall have that effect; or it is otherwise established that those States were agreed that the exchange of instruments should have that effect. States may also contract with each other under their domestic laws.

A treaty enters into force when the number of ratifications as specified in that treaty is received by the depository. When a treaty enters into force it is in force for only those States who have consented to be bound by it which are called "Parties".[33] However, an expression by a State that it consents to be bound by a particular treaty does not mean that *ipso facto* that treaty enters into force for that State. Either, the treaty must already be in force at that time, or as already mentioned the number of ratifications must be deposited. The Vienna Convention is more specific when it says that a treaty enters into force in such manner and upon such date as it may provide or as the negotiating States may agree.[34] There are three ways in which a treaty may enter into force. They are: on a date specified in the treaty; on signature only, as agreed by the negotiating States; or on ratification by all or a specified number of States. A treaty may be considered to apply to a State provisionally when the treaty itself so provides; or the negotiating States have in some other manner so agreed. Unless the treaty otherwise provides or the negotiating States have otherwise agreed, the provisional application of a treaty or a part of a treaty with respect to a State will be considered as terminated if that State notifies the other States between which the treaty is being applied provisionally of its intention not to become a party to the treaty.[35]

Once a State ratifies a treaty it has to deposit instruments of ratification with the United Nations or with the specialized agency of the United Nations as prescribed in the treaty concerned. Such Instruments must emanate from and be signed by the Head of State, Head of Government or Minister for Foreign Affairs or a person exercising, *ad interim*, the powers of one of the above authorities; clearly identify the treaty concerned and the type of action consistent with the provisions of the treaty, i.e., ratification, acceptance, approval, accession, consent to be bound, etc.; contain an unambiguous expression of the will of the Government, acting on

---

[32] Article 12 (1) states that the consent of a State to be bound by a treaty is expressed by the signature of its representative when: (*a*) the treaty provides that signature shall have that effect; (*b*) it is otherwise established that the negotiating States were agreed that signature should have that effect; or (*c*) the intention of the State to give that effect to the signature appears from the full powers of its representative or was expressed during the negotiation. Article 12.2 provides that for the purposes of paragraph 1: (*a*) the initialling of a text constitutes a signature of the treaty when it is established that the negotiating States so agreed; (*b*) the signature ad referendum of a treaty by a representative, if confirmed by his State, constitutes a full signature of the treaty.

[33] Vienna Convention, *supra* note 12 at Article 2 (1) (g). It should be noted that such States should not be called "signatories" as some refer to them erroneously.

[34] *Id*. Article 24 (1).

[35] *Id*. Article 25.

behalf of the State, to recognize itself as being bound by the treaty concerned and to undertake faithfully to observe and implement its provisions (a simple reference to a domestic statutory provision will be inadequate); indicate the title of the signatory. In the case of a person exercising, *ad interim*, the powers of the Head of State, Head of Government or Minister for Foreign Affairs, the title must indicate that the person is exercising such powers *ad interim*. In this respect, the depositary accepts the following formulations: Acting Head of State, Acting Head of Government, Acting Minister for Foreign Affairs, Head of State *ad interim*, Head of Government ad interim and Minister for Foreign Affairs ad interim. There must be an indication of the date and place where the instrument was issued.

If required, the instrument of deposit must specify the scope of its application in accordance with the provisions of the relevant treaty; and contain all mandatory declarations and notifications in accordance with the provisions of the relevant treaty. Where reservations are intended, such reservations since reservations must be signed by the Head of State, Head of Government or Minister for Foreign Affairs or a person exercising, ad interim, the powers of one of the above authorities.

A significant aspect of treaty law is the difference between a treaty and a memorandum of understanding (MOU). The fundamental difference between the two instruments lies in the terminology, and the fact that a treaty establishes legally binding obligations whereas an MOU or any other agreement such as a memorandum of cooperation (MOC), arrangement or exchange of letters does not create such obligations *stricto* sensu. A treaty would contain such language as "shall", "undertake", and "rights", whereas an MOC or other agreement would use the word "will" and avoid "shall" and "undertake". Treaties enter into force (usually when the required number of ratifications is received) whereas instruments such as MOUs and MOCs become applicable. However, a delicate nuance in the practice of treaty law is that merely because a particular instrument contains typical words used in a treaty, it may not necessarily be a treaty. Conversely, the use of the word "will" may not always mean that the Parties to a treaty did not intend to create a legally binding obligation.

The distinction between instruments that are conventionally recognized as treaties in accordance with the criteria discussed above, and other documents, has been blurred in practice. In the 1994 case of *Qatar* v. *Bahrain* the International Court of Justice went on to identify as a treaty a double exchange of letters i.e. between Bahrain and Saudi Arabia on the one hand and between Qatar and Saudi Arabia on the other, together with minutes of a meeting (held in 1990) between representatives of the three States and signed by the foreign Ministers of each State.

International Law and the United Nations

Purpose of the United Nations

The United Nations functions on treaties and resolutions of its General Assembly and Security Council. Treaties are essentially agreements between States, as already discussed. The organs of the United Nations such as its Specialized Agencies,[36] are established by States through treaties. The United Nations System (which includes the United Nations and its specialized agencies) primarily assert themselves through Resolutions adopted through their fora: The General Assembly; the Security Council (in the case of the United Nations); and Assemblies and Councils of the Specialized Agencies.

In addition to these bodies under the United Nations system, there is also the judicial organ—The International Court of Justice (ICJ) [37] which settles, in accordance with international law, legal disputes submitted to it by States and to give advisory opinions on legal questions referred to it by authorized United Nations organs and specialized agencies.[38] The mandate of the ICJ is enshrined in Article 33 of the United Nations Charter which admits of settlements of disputes between States by negotiation, enquiry, mediation, conciliation, arbitration, judicial settlement, and resort to regional agencies or arrangements. The good offices of the ICJ are also sought in appealing to third parties. For example, mediation places the parties to a dispute in a position in which they can themselves resolve their dispute thanks to the intervention of a third party. Arbitration goes further, in the sense that the dispute is submitted to the decision or award of an impartial third party, so that a binding settlement can be achieved. The same is true of judicial

---

[36] Article 57 of the United Nations Charter provides that the various specialized agencies, established by intergovernmental agreement and having wide international responsibilities, as defined in their basic instruments, in economic, social, cultural, educational, health, and related fields, shall be brought into relationship with the United Nations in accordance with the provisions of Article 63. Article 57 goes on to say that such agencies thus brought into relationship with the United Nations are referred to as specialized agencies.

[37] The International Court of Justice (ICJ) is the principal judicial organ of the United Nations (UN). It was established in June 1945 by the Charter of the United Nations and began work in April 1946. The seat of the Court is at the Peace Palace in The Hague (Netherlands). Of the six principal organs of the United Nations, it is the only one not located in New York (United States of America). The Court is composed of 15 judges, who are elected for terms of office of 9 years by the United Nations General Assembly and the Security Council. It is assisted by a Registry, its administrative organ. Its official languages are English and French.

[38] The genesis of the ICJ lay in Article 14 of the Covenant of the League of Nations which gave the Council of the League responsibility for formulating plans for the establishment of a Permanent Court of International Justice (PCIJ), such a court to be competent not only to hear and determine any dispute of an international character submitted to it by the parties to the dispute, but also to give an advisory opinion upon any dispute or question referred to it by the Council or by the Assembly. It remained for the League Council to take the necessary action to give effect to Article 14.

settlement (the method applied by the International Court of Justice), except that a court is subject to stricter rules than an arbitral tribunal, particularly in procedural matters.

The fundamental issue *in limine* is whether resolutions adopted by the United Nations bodies form hard law which States are legally bound to adhere to. *Brownlie* has expressed the view that decisions by international conferences and organizations can in principle only bind those States accepting them (Ian Brownlie 1990). Shaw, referring to the binding force of United Nations General Assembly Resolutions states:

> ...one must be alive to the dangers in ascribing legal value to everything that emanates from the Assembly. Resolutions are often the results of political compromises and arrangements and, comprehended in that sense, never intended to constitute binding norms. Great care must be taken in moving from a plethora of practice to the identification of legal norms (Shaw 2003).

With regard to the practice of other international organizations, a little more caution might be required, as a resolution might create a custom. Non binding instruments form a special category that is sometimes referred to as "soft law" which is definitely not law in the sense of enforceability.[39]

Herein lies the fundamental problem that blurs the legitimacy of the United Nations. On the one hand the United Nations is about global governance through international law. Governance in its basic sense is a set of principles and responsibilities that move in a strategic direction, and that direction, according to Article 1 of the Charter of the United Nations is to maintain international peace and security by taking effective collective measures for the prevention and removal of threats to the peace, and to suppress acts of aggression or other breaches of the peace, and to bring about by peaceful means, and in conformity with the principles of justice and international law, to adjust or settle international disputes or situations which might lead to a breach of the peace. The provision goes on to add to this strategic direction the task of developing friendly relations among nations based on respect for the principle of equal rights and self-determination of peoples, and taking other appropriate measures to strengthen universal peace; achieving international co-operation in solving international problems of an economic, social, cultural, or humanitarian character, and in promoting and encouraging respect for human rights and for fundamental freedoms for all without distinction as to race, sex, language, or religion; and to be a centre for harmonizing the actions of nations in the attainment of these common ends.

However, the United Nations often takes decision with or without the consent of the people of the world, which prompted one commentator to say that "global governance is a tyranny speaking the language of democracy" (George Monbiot 2007). This notwithstanding, one cannot say that the United Nations has been totally inept or ineffective in pursuing with some degree of commitment its

---

[39] *Id.* 111. See also A.J.P Tammes, *Decisions of International Organs as a Source of international Law*, 94 HR 1958 at 265.

fundamental responsibility to "maintain international peace" through the application of the principles of international law. Armed conflict in the current context brings to bear two overriding facts: The first is that the majority of the world's conflicts today take place within States rather than between them. The second is that when one looks at the peacemaking and peacekeeping roles of the United Nations, there is no room for doubt that the Organization's activities in this regard have been truly global. The Secretary General of the United Nations, Kofi Annan, in his Interim Report on the Prevention of Armed Conflict, presented to the 58th Session of the United Nations in December 2003, stated that the main responsibility for prevention of armed conflict lies with Governments rather than the international community. However, since its inception, the United Nations system has been increasingly called upon by States to assist them in the face of armed conflict within their territories. In pursuance of this continuing trend, the United Nations has used diplomatic means to prevent and resolve armed conflicts, whether between nations or within nations. The Department of Political Affairs (DPA) is responsible within the U.N. Secretariat for identifying threats to peace and attendant peacemaking opportunities. The Department also supports the Secretary-General and his special envoys in bringing "good offices" to bear in trying to broker agreements between parties involved in conflict situations.

UN peacemaking reached its peak in the 1990s, as the end of the Cold War gave the world community an impetus to find new opportunities to end civil wars through negotiated peace settlements. A large number of conflicts were brought to an end, either through direct UN mediation or by the efforts of other third parties acting with UN support. The UN success list includes El Salvador, Guatemala, Namibia, Cambodia, Mozambique, Tajikistan, Bougainville, Afghanistan, Sierra Leone, Burundi and the North-South conflict in Sudan.

Recent research reflects that expanded UN peacemaking, peacekeeping and conflict prevention activities has been a major influence in attaining a 40 % decline in armed conflict around the world since the 1990s. This includes an undetermined number of potential conflicts which have been defused through preventive diplomacy and other forms of preventive action.

The United Nations Department of Political Affaires, whose main mission is conflict prevention, which is one of the highest aims of the United Nations, once had the quote of United Nations Secretary General Kofi Annan, "No task is more fundamental to the United Nations than the prevention and resolution of deadly conflict". This is a quote from the Secretary General's speech *"In Larger Freedom: Towards Development, Security and Human Rights for All"*, delivered on 21 March 2005. The Secretary General has observed that both the nature and the UNs understanding of conflict have evolved since the goal of saving future generations "from the scourge of war" was enshrined in the Charter of the United Nations in 1945.

The mission of the Department of Political Affairs is based on the fundamental premise that, in today's world, preventive action extends well beyond traditional preventive diplomacy to involve a broad spectrum of U.N. entities working across a wide range of disciplines—poverty-eradication and development, human rights and the rule of law, elections and the building of democratic institutions, the control of small arms, to name just a few.

One of the countries in the South Asian region that the Department focussed on is Nepal, where there had been increasing concern about the internal situation in the country. Fighting had gone on in Nepal since 1996 between government forces and Maoist insurgents which has killed thousands while forcing many more to flee their homes. The suspension of constitutional rule and assumption of direct rule by the King had added to the complexity of the crisis. A monitoring mission of the Office of the High Commissioner for Human Rights was established during 2005 to help address a deteriorating situation. The Department managed the diplomatic track, supporting efforts of the Secretary-General to promote a political negotiated settlement to the conflict and a return to constitutional rule after its dissolution in February 2005.

The Department of Political Affairs closely monitored developments in the country while engaging in constant discussion with a broad range of Nepali and regional actors—urging a negotiated political solution and offering the good offices of the Secretary-General. DPA provided support to high level diplomatic efforts by the Secretary-General's Special Adviser, Lakhdar Brahimi, including during his July 2005 visit to Nepal in which he urged an end to hostilities, a prompt return to constitutional rule and national dialogue to resolve the serious crisis in the country.

Similarly, in Myanmar the United Nations sought to help bring about a return to democracy and improved human rights though an all-inclusive process of national reconciliation. The role of the Department of Political Affairs, in addition to monitoring and assessing political developments in the country, was to provide substantive staff support to the good offices mission of the Secretary-General and his Special Envoy for Myanmar, established in successive General Assembly resolutions adopted since Myanmar's military leadership voided the results of democratic elections in 1990. However, the Secretary-General's good offices efforts encountered considerable difficulties since the ouster of the former Prime Minister General Khin Nyunt, and his associates, in the fall of 2004. Special Envoy Ambassador Razali Ismail stepped down in January 2006 after having been unable to visit the country for nearly 2 years. Nonetheless Secretary-General Annan remained committed to providing his good offices, including through contacts occurring outside of Myanmar. He took every available opportunity to urge the Government to free arrested dissidents including Daw Aung San Suu Kyi, to ease restrictions on the National League for Democracy and other parties, and to include all ethnic nationality groups and political leaders in national dialogue, in the writing of a new constitution and in other established steps along the path toward national reconciliation and the full restoration of democracy.

Going on to another conflict ridden region, Central Asia, the United Nations has recognized that helping the region to consolidate peace and prevent future conflict is a major challenge for the international community, given the explosive array of problems facing the five nations of the region. Poverty, authoritarian rule, inter-ethnic tensions, and the growth of organized crime and religious extremism are among the factors contributing to growing tensions and turbulence. Building a durable peace in Tajikistan after that country's devastating 5-year civil war was its own unique and formidable task.

The Department of Political Affairs is deeply involved in U.N. efforts to help Central Asia come to grips with these challenges. The United Nations Tajikistan Office of Peace-(UNTOP) building, deployed since 2000, is one of the peace-building support offices supervised and supported by DPA. The Department has also spearheaded U.N. efforts to promote greater regional cooperation on common problems, through the Forum for Conflict Prevention in Central Asia.

UNTOP, was established in 2000, following on from the work of a U.N. peacekeeping mission. Among its initiatives, the Office promotes dialogue across Tajik society, provides training on conflict prevention, human rights and the rule of law, and has also helped the authorities to strengthen Tajikistan's electoral institutions.

In extending UNTOP's mandate of the Mission through mid-2006 Secretary-General Kofi Annan noted both the progress and the challenges ahead for Tajikistan, saying that "During the past 5 years of peace building, Tajik society has come a long way in healing the wounds of civil war. However, much remains to be done in strengthening national unity and consolidating peace."

On to the Arab world, the Secretary General of the United Nations, in his message to the Summit of the League of Arab States held in Khartoum, Sudan, on 28 March 2006—stated that the delegates were gathered during a period of con-tinued turbulence in the Arab world and the surrounding region, and thus of many formidable challenges for them. He added that in Iraq, while the main benchmarks of the transition timetable have been met, the situation remained dangerous and unstable. The United Nations continues to believe that an inclusive and transparent political process offers the best prospects for improving security, safeguarding human rights, consolidating gains towards democracy and improving the welfare of the Iraqi people. Therefore, the Secretary General urged all concerned to move swiftly to form a fully inclusive Government. He assured that the United Nations will continue to promote inter-communal dialogue and support the constitutional review process, as well as the Arab League initiative to convene a Conference on Iraqi National Accord, all of which offer opportunities to forge a broader national consensus. The Secretary General pledged that the United Nations will also maintain its efforts, as circumstances permit, to assist the reconstruction and the economic development of Iraq, since. He also said that Iraq's integration into the wider region must be another priority. A challenge was posed to Iraq's neighbours to make every effort to support the peace process by refraining from interference in the country's internal affairs, and to uphold its unity and territorial integrity.

The United Nation also recognizes that the conflict between Israelis and Pal-estinians is at a critical stage. The decision of the Palestinian people in the 2008 parliamentary elections, whose conduct the United Nations believed was a credit to Palestinian democracy, brought new hope, that the new government in the occupied Palestinian territory would address the Palestinian people's aspirations for peace and statehood, which were articulated by President Abbas.

For its part, the United Nations has undertaken to continue to work for an end to the occupation that began in 1967 and a settlement of the conflict in accordance with Security Council Resolutions. Until that goal is achieved, Secretary General Annan said the UN would discharge the mandates entrusted to it by the Member States to assist the Palestinian people. The UN also pressed for the easing of the severe closures in Gaza and the West Bank, which the United Nations carefully documents, and which cause severe hardships and humiliations. In a strong statement he reminded all UN states that the Palestinian people should not be punished for the way they exercise their democratic rights, and that their precious institutions remain the foundation for building a Palestinian State that can live side by side in peace with a secure Israel and all its neighbours.

Somalia, another country which was plagued with internal violence, continues to draw the attention of the United Nations. The weakness or non-existence of governing institutions, and a lack of national consensus on the future, continue to be a matter of concern to the UN. The UN believes that, as long as force is used to resolve grievances or to further political objectives, gains would be fragile and the country's recovery will be impossible. The United Nations, for its part, has assured Somalia and the world community that it will continue to provide political, moral and material support for the transitional process.

The United Nations has played a role in bringing about independence in countries that are now among its Member States. Since 1945, the United Nations has been credited with negotiating 172 peaceful settlements that have ended regional conflicts. Recent cases include an end to the Iran–Iraq war, the withdrawal of Soviet troops from Afghanistan, and an end to the civil war in El Salvador. The United Nations has used quiet diplomacy to avert imminent wars. An example of this is the deployment of a total of 63 peace-keeping forces and observer missions from its inception to date, by which the United Nations has been able to restore calm to allow the negotiating process to go forward while saving millions of people from becoming casualties of conflicts. There were active peace-keeping forces and one special political mission in operation at the time of writing.

The United Nations remains ready and vigilant to assist States in their peace-making and peacekeeping activities. In his Report referred to earlier in this article, Secretary General Annan referred to four complimentary trends: The first is that most of the United Nations system has accepted conflict prevention and resolution as a key activity that has been increasingly integrated into the mandates of various UN bodies; the second trend is that there is increased capacity in the system to move forward at the country level and to mobilize the resources of the UN system in a coordinated fashion; the third is that there is increased willingness in the United Nations to develop integrated strategies on conflict prevention and peace-building cooperation between UN headquarters and the field units and the last is that there is the will to move towards multi-dimensional and log-term approaches to conflict prevention.

General Assembly Resolution 57/337 of July 2003 on the Prevention of Armed Conflict recognized that the pacific settlement of disputes and prevention of armed conflict is a useful tool for the United Nations with which it could build a solid foundation for peace. It also reaffirmed the primary responsibility for preventing armed conflict, encouraging them to develop strategies. At the same time the Resolution recognized the role that the United Nations could play in assisting member States achieve domestic and external harmony. With all this having been accomplished, one cannot justifiably say that States are destitute of assistance from the outside world and the community of nations if they are ever in need of help to bring peace into their lands.

The Secretary General

The Secretary General of the United Nations is the executive head of the United Nations—a highly diverse organization working worldwide to improve the lives, living standards and health of those needing help. He/she is appointed by the General Assembly upon recommendation of the Security Council. This is provided for by Article 97 of the United Nations Charter which also stipulates that the UN Secretariat shall comprise a Secretary-General and such staff as the Organization may require and that the Secretary-General shall be the chief administrative officer of the Organization. The Secretariat is comprised of some 8,700 regular civilian staff members in the UN Headquarters in New York as well as around the world in UN offices, all of whom report to the Secretary General. The overall staff strength of the United Nations would rise to approximately 50,000 if the specialized agencies of the United Nations and the financial institutions based in Washington D.C. such as the World Bank are to be taken into consideration. The Secretary General overseas a $5 billion peacekeeping budget which sustains over 80,000 peacekeepers worldwide.

The Secretary General (and his staff) are granted a number of privileges and immunities, including exemption from national service obligations, immunity from lawsuits for acts performed in an official capacity and exemption from direct taxes on salaries and emoluments. The Secretary General is assisted by the Deputy Secretary General and several Under Secretaries General, special envoys and assistant Secretaries General in that order. The Secretary General and his immediate assistants are elevated to the same level as diplomatic envoys.

The Secretary-General could serve for one or two terms of 5 years each. Traditionally the Secretary-General cannot be a national of any of the permanent Security Council nations. The post loosely follows a cycle in which each successive Secretary-General comes from a different continent. The current Secretary-General is Ban Ki-Moon of South Korea who is the eighth Secretary General. His appointment began on January 1 2007.

Shortly after taking office, Secretary General Ban Ki-moon's predecessor in office, Kofi Annan presented a sweeping reform package aimed at helping the United Nations to change with the times and adapt to a new era of global affairs. Reform measures falling under the authority of the Secretary-General had been largely implemented or set in motion; they had been administrative—such as a zero-growth budget and rigorous efforts to upgrade management practices—as well as organizational, with the emphasis on enabling the Organization to respond more effectively to the growing demands placed on it, particularly in the areas of development and peacekeeping.

One of the most vital roles played by the Secretary-General is the use of his "good offices"—steps taken publicly and in private, drawing upon his independence, impartiality and integrity, to prevent international disputes from arising, escalating or spreading. Since becoming Secretary-General, Mr. Annan made use of his good offices in a range of situations, involving among other nations Cyprus, East Timor, Iraq, Libya, Nigeria and Western Sahara.

The position of Secretary General is, by unwritten convention, expected to rotate by geographic region. When Annan had finished his first term, the member states were so impressed with his performance that he was appointed for a second term despite a general feeling that the next Secretary-General should have been from Asia. There has not yet been a Secretary-General from North America, Eastern Europe or Oceania.

The Secretary-General ultimately appointed is usually a candidate considered consensually acceptable to the Security Council and is therefore recommended by the Security Council to the General Assembly. Any candidate would not be appointed if there were to be even a single veto against him or her from a member of the Security Council. Usually, the successful candidate is from a middle power who has little or no claim to prior fame. Although high-profile candidates are often mentioned as worthy of the job, they are almost always rejected as unacceptable to some. For instance, figures like Charles de Gaulle, Dwight Eisenhower and Anthony Eden were considered for the first Secretary-General position, but were rejected in favour of the uncontroversial Norwegian Trygve Lie. It is felt that owing to the vagaries of international politics and intrigues of political compromise, there are many similarities between the process and ideals for selecting the Secretary-General and those of selecting leading figures in other international organizations.

It was originally felt that the role of the Secretary-General should be purely administrative. This trend was changed by the first Secretary-General Trygve Lie who asserted that it behoved the Secretary General to speak out and act as leader and mediator. Each of his successors, following this approach, has spoken out on global issues and used the good offices of the Secretary General to mediate disputes. This is consistent with the original vision of U.S. President Franklin D. Roosevelt, who held office just before the creation of the UN and had much influence on its shaping, that the organization should be headed by a "world moderator.

In addition to managing staff and administering them, the Secretary-General plays a key role in mediation between States, negotiating between warring parties and deploying UN sponsored peace keeping forces. The Secretary-General also appoints special envoys and personal representatives who undertake missions in difficult areas. By March 2006 there were no less than 60 such special envoys.

The Secretary General who is in equal parts diplomat, advocate, civil servant and CEO, remains the bulwark of United Nations ideals and a spokesman for the welfare and interests of the people of the world. Much the Secretary General's focus on the poor, the downtrodden and vulnerable.

The Secretary-General's day to day tasks include attendance at sessions of United Nations bodies; consultations with world leaders, government officials, and others; and worldwide travel intended to keep him in touch with the peoples of the Organization's Member States and informed about the vast array of issues of international concern that are on the Organization's agenda. Each year, the Secretary-General issues a report on the work of the United Nations that appraises its activities and outlines future priorities. The Secretary-General is also Chairman of the Administrative Committee on Coordination (ACC), which brings together the Executive Heads of all UN funds, programmes and specialized agencies twice a year in order to further coordination and cooperation in the entire range of substantive and management issues facing the United Nations System.

One of the empowering provisions in the United Nations Charter which assigns a signal role to the Secretary-General is Article 99 which enables the Secretary-General to bring to the attention of the Security Council any matter which in his/her opinion may threaten the maintenance of international peace and security. Notable examples of instances when this Article was used relate to the Congo, when Dag Hammarskjold cautioned the Security Council, followed by Trygve Lie in Korea and Kurt Waldheim in Iran. Although this provision has not been frequently used, the Secretary-General can, without invoking the provision, exert his influence behind the scenes with the States, in particular the powers in the Security Council. The eight Secretaries General who have so far been at the helm during the United Nations' 60 years of existence have demonstrated that their personal judgment, initiative and risk taking ability are the defining qualities of a Secretary-General.

The Secretary General is subject to continued scrutiny and criticism of States. For example, Secretary General U Thant was held accountable and was stringently criticized for pulling out troops from the Sinai in 1967. Similarly, both Secretaries General Lie and Hammarskjold were criticized by the Soviet bloc for the actions taken in Korea and the Congo respectively. In more recent years Secretary-General Perez de Cuellar was criticized for his role in the Persian Gulf as well as Boutros-Ghali regarding Bosnia, and Kofi Annan with regard to the UN role in Somalia and Iraq. Criticism is an integral corollary of the job, although through the years, the Secretary General has not come out with a harsh judgment that would reflect his partisanship which in turn would result in the loss of his credibility and confidence of powerful and important States.

One of the official duties of the Secretary General is to manage the budget of the United Nations which is comprised of contributions from member States. Both estimated incomes and estimated expenditures are laid down in the Organization's budget by the various administrative organs of the UN. The Secretary General compiles these various proposals and sends them to several advisory bodies for their views and revisions after which the document passes on to the Plenary. The budget is of critical importance to the Secretary General as the availability of funds and resources could well contribute to timely action on the part of the UN in crisis situations where, often the complaint is made that the UN does not deliver what it promises.

The seminal characteristic of the office of the Secretary General lies in its neutrality and the lack of vested interests. The Secretary General does not, under any circumstance "enforce" but rather overseas the facilitation of administration in States that need such support after collapsing or succumbing to natural or manmade disasters and wars.

Neither the Secretary General nor the staff of the United Nations Secretariat and other offices are allowed to seek or follow instructions from any government or State. They are international civil servants driven by their own impartiality and independence. The UN Charter, under Article 96 allows only the General Assembly and the Security Council to seek an advisory opinion from the judicial organ of the UN, the International Court of Justice. The office of the Secretary General has in the past sought a mandate to request such opinions from the ICJ under this provision, on the ground that an opinion from the world court, when solicited by the head of the UN and delivered, would assist him in defining legitimate positions of the international community in situations that present a threat to world peace.

The issue of human rights has been paramount under both the Annan and ki-Moon administrations. It is noteworthy that until Secretary General Annan took over as head of the UN there was not much emphasis on human rights. Therefore, Secretary General Annan's commitment and dedication to human rights have effectively percolated to his successor as an inheritance that comes with the job.

The question arises as to whether the General assembly, which appoints the Secretary General, can interfere or affect the functions of the Secretary General. The answer seems to lie in the opinion delivered by the International Court of Justice with regard to the creation of the United Nations Administrative Tribunal (UNAT). When the UNAT was created by the General Assembly in the 1940s as a court to hear disputes between the UN staff and the Secretary General, and the UNAT started handing down judgments that required the Secretary General to pay compensation to aggrieved staff, the Secretary General requested the General Assembly for a separate budgetary allotment to pay the awards. The General Assembly refused this request stating that the Assembly was not bound by the judgments of the UNAT. One of the arguments placed before the International Court of Justice was that by creating the UNAT the General Assembly interfered with the powers and functions of the Secretary General. The ICJ rejected this argument, stating that the General Assembly, by virtue of Article 101 of the UN Charter, had powers to establish staff rules for the UN staff and therefore had the power to interfere with the Secretary General's work.

What faces the Secretary General in the 21st Century? To answer this question, one has to take note of Secretary-General Kofi Annan's vision of "the three pillars" around which we need to reorganise today's United Nations to give it focus, to reconnect it and make it more relevant to its core constituents: the peoples of the world. These three pillars are: development; security and human rights; and democracy. Secretary General Ban Ki-Moon has pledged to lead by example; seek excellence with humility; set the highest ethical standard; pursue dialogue and engagement; play the role of harmonizer and bridge-builder; make transparency and accountability the cornerstone of my tenure; be animated by both passion and compassion in achieving our goals; and be sensitive to the concerns of all Member States, big and small.

Prevention of armed conflict and mending fences after an armed conflict that cannot be prevented are major issues for the Secretary General. Armed conflict remains the primary source of instability today and is therefore incontrovertibly the main concern of the United Nations. There is no room for doubt that responsibility for the prevention of armed conflict lies with the States themselves. However, this does not absolve the United Nations of all responsibility, particularly as most conflicts today occur within States and the United Nations has the capacity to assist States in adopting preventive measures. Also, arguably, the most serious current threat to humankind is the use of nuclear weapons. The threat is further exacerbated by the fact that materials and technology used to produce nuclear weapons may be increasingly passing on to the hands of non-State parties, including terrorist organizations. In this context, the United Nations and its member nations cannot entirely rule out the possibility of a large scale use of nuclear weapons. This perhaps is the most daunting prospect for the current and the next Secretary General.

The development of international law is one of the main tasks of the United Nations. However, the biggest dilemma that the Organization is facing is the dichotomy between law and legitimacy. Being the only truly global institution that can lay claims to universal legitimacy as a uniting force among its 193 member States, it has to ensure that the conduct of States accords with the fundamental sources of international law as contained in Article 38(1) of its Charter. One commentator, citing the glaring distinction between law and legitimacy through the example of the election of the current Secretary General, states:

> The reason for the underestimation of the extent and gravity of the gap [between law and legitimacy] may be that separate segments of the international community have problems with disparate elements of the gap. The result is a failure to capture the different dimensions in their cumulatively devastating impact on the UN's self proclaimed legitimacy. I draw attention to the risks of the growing gap with respect to UN sanctions, the challenge of nuclear weapons, the use of force, international criminal justice, the structure and procedures of the Security Council, and accountability deficits among UN officials (Thakur 2010).

United Nations Secretary General Ban Ki-Moon, at a press briefing on 22 January 2013 in New York, stressed that his approach to the role and functions of the United Nations was preventive diplomacy, which he placed second in priority to sustainable development. The Secretary General, in his prioritizing of sustainable development obviously meant the classic definition adopted by the United Nations (first introduced by a Report called "Our Common Future", also known as the Brundtland Report, published by the United Nations World Commission on

Environment and Development (WCED) in 1987): "Sustainable development is development that meets the needs of the present without compromising the ability of future generations to meet their own needs. Sustainable development contains within it two key concepts: the concept of needs, in particular the essential needs of the world's poor, to which overriding priority should be given; and the idea of limitations imposed by the state of technology and social organization on the environment's ability to meet present and future needs.

The United Nations has its Millennium Goals, which should be reached by 2015. These goals address the world's needs, starting with the need for the alleviation of poverty. Curiously, the Secretary General, in his address prior to the press briefing, said that he was on his way to Kuwait to seek pledges of donor nations that would provide much needed funds for the next 6 months to provide for the refugees of Syria, the need being $1.5 billion. Lakhdar Brahimi, Joint Special Representative of the United Nations and the League of Arab States to Syria, in an interview on 30 January 2013 stated that Syria—a country in which no one went hungry prior to the current conflict—had 25 % of its people in dire need. At the time of writing this percentage had grown exponentially.

The following figures are also relevant: Half the world's 7,000,000,000 people live on less than $2.00 a day. Over one billion people heralded the 21st century totally illiterate; The GDP (Gross Domestic Product) of the poorest 48 nations (of the world's countries) is less than the combined wealth of the world's 3 richest people. Nearly 1,000,000,000 people entered the 21st century unable to read a book or sign their names.; and 51 % of the world's 100 wealthiest bodies are corporations. The wealthiest nation on Earth has the widest gap between rich and poor of any industrialized nation; The poorer the country, the more likely that its debt repayments are being taken from people who neither contracted the loans nor received any of the money; 20 % of the population in developed nations consume 86 % of the world's goods; The top 20 % of people living in the richest countries enjoy 82 % of export trade and 68 % of foreign direct investment. The bottom 20 % of people barely receive more than 1 %; and in 1960, the 20 % of people in the richest countries had 30 times the income of the poorest 20 %. In 1997, that ratio increased to 74 times as much.

Jeffrey Sachs, onetime Special Advisor to former United Nations Secretary General Kofi Annan on the UN Millennium Development Goals and Economic Advisor to Governments around the World states without reservation that by 2025, we could be totally poverty-free by using the wealth of the world and the power of unending repositories of knowledge that we have (Sachs 2005). Of course, as every good news has a caveat, Sachs lays down the condition that our ability to transcend global poverty would depend on our collective wisdom in using our resources prudently and with good judgment. In his book, Sachs shows the way towards charting a wiser path towards global wealth and prosperity.

It is quite obvious that, from now until 2015 the United Nations has a daunting task. In the central theme of the Millennium Goals lies the belief of States that the fundamental challenge to be faced today is to ensure that globalization becomes a positive force for all the world's people. For while globalization offers great opportunities, at present its benefits are very unevenly shared, while its costs are unevenly distributed. There is overall recognition that developing countries and countries with economies in transition face special difficulties in responding to this central challenge. Thus, only through broad and sustained efforts to create a shared future, based upon common humanity in all its diversity, can globalization be made fully inclusive and equitable. States are resolved that these efforts must include policies and measures, at the global level, which correspond to the needs of developing countries and economies in transition and are formulated and implemented with their effective participation.

States have also recognized, through the Millennium Goals certain fundamental values to be essential to international relations in the 21st century. These include freedom, equality, solidarity, tolerance, respect for nature, shared responsibility, and peace and security. One of the results of the Millennium Goals was an "Outcome Document" adopted by global leaders at a High Level Plenary Meeting of the UN General Assembly in 2005. This document calls for a high level coordination between the various UN specialized agencies, resulting in a stronger system-wide coherence, particularly across the various development related agencies, funds and programs of the United Nations. Secretary General Kofi Annan has commissioned a group of international experts to take the Outcome Document forward in ensuring stronger coordination in humanitarian assistance, environmental activities and development.

With all these, the United Nations also has to practice what the Secretary General called "preventive diplomacy". He said the United Nations should not be considered a "global fire station" that would douse fires whenever they flamed across the world. Instead the Organization should prevent catastrophes and conflicts and prevent the world from plunging into want and suffering.

One has to place both the UN and the global community of nations in perspective. The history of mankind has proved that it is part of human nature to learn from past experience. That having been said, we have also acted with foresight in situations where we could not build on past experience. When we look at the history of international relations, we see that we have acted with foresight, as a result of which we have brought about major changes to the international legal system by reacting to past disasters. The United Nations was built on the failure of the League of Nations which was set up as a reaction to World War 1. The failure of the League of Nations was that its Covenant, although intended to prevent the recurrence of atrocities of 1914, failed to outlaw war but merely provided procedures for the peaceful settlement of disputes. Creators of the United Nations learnt from this mistake and wrote into the Charter of the UN the principle of collective security. The UN Security Council, on behalf of the entirety of UN member States, was empowered by the Charter to take decisive action against delinquents. However, this has never worked in practice when it was most needed. For example, the Security Council was literally impotent during the height of the Cold War. The Security Council has not taken or enforced military action against delinquent States nor has it received military assistance from member States to implement the powers ascribed to the Security Council by the UN Charter.

The reactions of the Security Council have allegedly been sporadic and reactive, authorizing member States to take action on its behalf, which has prompted one commentator to say that the Council has not acted or functioned as a constitutional framework for a peaceful world but rather as a fire department reacting to emergencies as they rise.

The above notwithstanding, to totally lay the blame at the doorstep of the United Nations for its inability to take action when required is analogous to blaming a medical doctor for the death of a patient who does not heed the doctor's advice. The prime offender in the current situation of the UN is international law or those who adopt international law, which are the member States of the United Nations. As discussed earlier in this article, one of the sources of public international law is the multilateral treaty through which States create law to be adhered to by the community of nations. Blatant examples of the reluctance of States to adopt international legislation in a timely fashion can be seen firstly with regard to the events of 11 September 2001, where, although there were repeated warnings by the Security Council prior to the events of the danger of a terrorist attack, and the Council called upon States to take effective action, particularly to ratify and implement existing security treaties, no action was taken. Another area of significant concern is the threat of nuclear weapons, which has been looming over several decades. Although the enormity of damage caused by nuclear devastation was apparent after the bombings of Hiroshima and Nagasaki in 1945, States have addressed this issue with inexplicable complacence and feckless insouciance. There is no existing treaty which outlaws or bans the use of nuclear weapons outright. The closest is the Comprehensive Nuclear-Test-Ban Treaty (CTBT) which bans all nuclear explosions in all environments, for military or civilian purposes. It was adopted by the United Nations General Assembly on 10 September 1996 but entered into force only on 27 September 2013. The Nuclear Non Proliferation Treaty merely preserves the oligopoly of nuclear powers as they exist at the present time. Article VI of the Treaty, which obliges States to negotiate with a view to achieving complete disarmament, remains a toothless tiger. Even the International Court of Justice, when requested for an opinion in July 1996 as to whether nuclear weapons and their use are against accepted principles of public international law, meandered to explain that there was no comprehensive and universal prohibition of the use of nuclear weapons, either in customary or conventional internal law.

Therefore, the question that arises is "when international law remains retrogressive in this manner, could one expect the United Nations to progress?" The root cause of the regress lies in the legislators or States themselves, who have not acted with foresight in the face of emergent threats and problems. Certainly, this somewhat bizarre collective disability is not characteristic of humanity, which has been quick to foresee the future. The unique nature of the international community, which is increasingly showing a tendency to ignore the experiences of others and the complexities of the modern world in finding a compromise to new and emergent issues, could well be the reason.

Given the unpredictability of the world, one of the greatest challenges faced by today's leadership is not so much the dilemma to choose between the alternative of making and not making, but of unmaking. As the old fable goes, the great Saturn, growing weary of sitting alone, and with no one but Heaven and Uranus watching him, created an oyster, and repeated this act several times, bringing forth a race of oysters. Watching this monotonous reluctance of Saturn's conservatism, Uranus cried out, "a new work, O Saturn! The old is not good again", to which Saturn replied that he feared he shall not do, but undo, and therefore he kept to safe acts. Later, Saturn thought, and thought, and the words of Uranus came to him like a burning ray of the Sun, and he created Jupiter. After that Saturn lapsed into his usual sloth and fear, and the world froze. To save the world, Jupiter slay his father, Saturn.

References

Brownlie I (1990) Principles of public international law, 4th edn. Clarendon Pres, Oxford, p 691

Greig DW (1976) International law, 2nd edn. Butterworths, London, p 8

Monbiot G (2007) The best way to give the poor a real voice is through a world parliament. The Guardian, London, p 31 (24 April 2007)

Reuter (1989) Introduction to the law of treaties. Pinter Publishers, London, New York, p 16

Sachs J (2005) The end of poverty—economic possibilities of our time. Penguin, New York, p 3

Schwarzenberger G, Brown ED (1976) A manual of international law, 6th edn. Professional Books Limited, Oxon, p 118

Shaw MN (2003) International law, 5th edn. Cambridge University Press, Cambridge, p 110

Thakur R (2010) Law, legitimacy and the United Nations. Melbourne J Int Law 11:1

von der Dunk FG (2014) Jus Cogens Sive Lex Ferenda: Jus Cogentium. In: Masson-Zwaan TL, Mendes De Leon PMJ (eds) Air and space law: De Lege Ferenda, essays in honour of Henri A. Wassenbergh vol 219. Martinus Nijhoff, Dordrecht, pp 223–224

Chapter 2
General Principles of Environmental Law and Regulation

Introduction

As a specialized agency of the United Nations, ICAO draws its legitimacy from the United Nations and any treaty or other agreement or arrangement that ICAO develops containing a global market based measure would have to accord with the meaning and purpose of the United Nations. It is for this reason that the previous chapter on the development of international law and the United Nations becomes essential background material for this study.

International environmental law did not come into being as a separate branch of public international law until a few decades ago. There were no texts on the subject and academic journals were bereft of any material on law and the environment particularly prior to 1072 when the Stockholm Conference[1] on the Environment took place. One commentator attributes this trend to apathy or the focus of interest by the international community on other pressing issues (Atapattu 2006). However, there has been much awareness, progress and evolution in the field of environmental law and regulation since 1972. To begin with, the Declaration adopted at the Stockholm Conference alerted the world to the importance of environmental protection, stating that man is both creature and moulder of his environment, which gives him physical sustenance and affords him the opportunity for intellectual, moral, social and spiritual growth. The Declaration went on to say that in the long and tortuous evolution of the human race on this planet a stage has been reached when, through the rapid acceleration of science and technology, man has acquired the power to transform his environment in countless ways and on an unprecedented scale. Both aspects of man's environment, the natural and the man-made, are essential to his well-being and to the enjoyment of basic human rights the right to life itself.

---

[1] United Nations Conference on the Human Environment, Stokholm, 1972. See UN. Doc. A/CONF.48/14 June 1972, reprinted in 11 ILM 1416 (1972).

© The Author(s) 2014
R. Abeyratne, *Aviation and Climate Change*, SpringerBriefs in Law,
DOI: 10.1007/978-3-319-08443-5_2

Arguably the most important pronouncement of the Stockholm Declaration lies the recognition enunciated in Principle 21, that States have, in accordance with the Charter of the United Nations, and the principles of international law, the sovereign right to exploit their own natural resources pursuant to their own environmental policies, and the responsibility to ensure that activities within their jurisdiction or control do not cause damage to the environment of other states or of areas beyond the limits of national jurisdiction.

Principle 21 therefore becomes the fundamental postulate of environmental law on which subsequent developments responding to environmental issues would hinge. However, it is important to note that the Principle also states that, although countries can exploit their natural resources and it is their sovereign right to do so, they should do so without harming the environment of other countries and the global environment. It is this caveat that has made Principle 21 to be known as the principle of harm prevention.

Some years earlier, the 1941 *Trail Smelter Arbitration*,[2] which addressed transboundary pollution between the United States and Canada applied this principle in a somewhat limited form. The commonality between Principle 21 and the *Trail Smelter* judgment is that both maintain the sovereign right of States to exploit their natural resources and both support the view that states should have the interests of neighbouring States at heart. The case, which involved damage caused to the United States by fumes emitted by a smelter in Canada and carried across to its neighbour, causing damage to human health and property, resulted in the judgment that under principles of international law, no State has the right to use or permit the use of territory in such a manner as to cause injury by fumes in or to the territory of another or the property of another or the properties of persons therein, when the case is of serious consequence and the injury is established by clear and convincing evidence. Many commentators argue that the *Trail Smelter* arbitration has limited relevance or application in the current context since many of the modern environmental issues and contentions no longer fit into the traditional conception of transboundary pollution as enunciated in the *Trail Smelter* case. Instead, States have obviated adjudication in preference of regulatory solutions. Some commentators are of the view that the areas of the arbitration that cause concern, particularly the endorsement on the right to pollute, have been forgotten, making the basic teachings of the case one of marginal relevance to modern international environmental law. Arguably, the most enduring principle brought to bear by the *Trail Smelter* arbitration is the supremacy of State sovereignty and the right of States to legislate on and regulate environmental protection within their territories.

---

[2] 3 RIAA 1905 (1941).

The principle of the Trail Smelter arbitration surfaced once again in the 1996 case pertaining to the *Legality of the Threat or Use of Nuclear Weapons*[3] when the International Court of Justice said:

> The existence of the general obligation of States to ensure that activities within their jurisdiction and control and respect the environment of other States or of areas beyond natural control, is now part of the corpus of international law relating to the environment.[4]

It is clear in the face of this judgment that the trail smelter principle of harm prevention imposes on all States an obligation erga omnes. Obligations arising from jus cogens are considered applicable erga omnes which would mean that States using their natural resources owe a duty of care to the world at large in the exploitation of such natural resources so as not to cause them harm. The ICJ in the *Barcelona Traction Case* held:

> [A]n essential distinction should be drawn between the obligations of a State towards the international community as a whole, and those arising vis a vis another State in the field of diplomatic protection. By their very nature, the former are the concerns of all States. In view of the importance of the rights involved, all States can be held to have a legal interest in their protection; they are obligations erga omnes.[5]

The International Law Commission has observed of the ICJ decision:

> [I]n the Courts view, there are in fact a number, albeit limited, of international obligations which, by reason of their importance to the international community as a whole, are— unlike others—obligations in respect of which all States have legal interest.[6]

The views of the ICJ and the International Law Commission, which has supported the approach taken by the ICJ, give rise to two possible conclusions relating to jus cogens and its resultant obligations erga omnes:

(a) obligations erga omnes affect all States and thus cannot be made inapplicable to a State or group of States by an exclusive clause in a treaty or other document reflecting legal obligations without the consent of the international community as a whole;

(b) obligations erga omnes pre-empt other obligations which may be incompatible with them.

---

[3] 1996 *ICJ* 226.

[4] Id. paragraph 29. In the celebrated *Corfu Channel* case which involved the liability of Albania for mine-layering in her international waters which caused space damage to British mine sweepers, the Court held:

> These grave omissions involve the international responsibility of Albania. The Court therefore reaches the conclusion that Albania is responsible under international law for the explosions which occurred ... and for the damage and loss of human life which resulted from them. See ICJ Reports (1949) at p. 23.

[5] *Barcelona Traction, Light and Power Company Limited, I.C.J. Reports, 1974, 253 at 269–270.*

[6] *Yearbook of International Law Commission 1976, Vol II, Part One at 29.*

Some examples of obligations erga omnes cited by the ICJ are prohibition of acts of aggression, genocide, slavery and discrimination. It is indeed worthy of note that all these obligations are derivatives of norms which are jus cogens at international law.

International responsibility relates both to breaches of treaty provisions and other breaches of legal duty. In the *Spanish Zone of Morocco Claims* case, Justice Huber observed:

> [R]esponsibility is the necessary corollary of a right. All rights of an international character involve international responsibility. If the obligation in question is not met, responsibility entails the duty to make reparation All rights of an international character involve international responsibility. If the obligation in question is not met, responsibility entails the duty to make reparation.[7]

It is also now recognized as a principle of international law that the breach of a duty involves an obligation to make reparation appropriately and adequately. This reparation is regarded as the indispensable complement of a failure to apply a convention and is applied as an inarticulate premise that need not be stated in the breached convention itself.[8] The ICJ affirmed this principle in 1949 in the *Corfu Channel* Case[9] by holding that Albania was responsible under international law to pay compensation to the United Kingdom for not warning that Albania had laid mines in Albanian waters which caused explosions, damaging ships belonging to the United Kingdom. Since the treaty law provisions of liability and the general principles of international law as discussed complement each other in endorsing the liability of States to compensate for damage caused by space objects, there is no contention as to whether in the use of nuclear power sources in outer space, damage caused by the uses of space objects or use thereof would not go uncompensated. Furthermore, under the principles of international law, moral damages based on pain, suffering and humiliation, as well as on other considerations, are considered recoverable (Christol 1991).

The sense of international responsibility that the United Nations ascribed to itself had reached a heady stage at this point, where the role of international law in international human conduct was perceived to be primary and above the authority of States. In its Report to the General Assembly, the International Law Commission recommended a draft provision which required:

> Every State has the duty to conduct its relations with other States in accordance with international law and with the principle that the sovereignty of each State is subject to the supremacy of international law.[10]

---

[7] *I.C.J. Reports*, 1970 at 32.

[8] *In Re. Chorzow Factory (Jurisdiction) Case, (1927) PCIJ, Ser. A, no. 9* at 21.

[9] *ICJ Reports (1949)*, 4 at 23.

[10] *Report of the International Law Commission to the General Assembly on the Work of the 1st Session, A/CN.4/13*, June 9 1949, at 21.

This principle, which forms a cornerstone of international conduct by States, provides the basis for strengthening international comity and regulating the conduct of States both internally—within their territories—and externally, towards other States. States are effectively precluded by this principle of pursuing their own interests untrammelled and with disregard to principles established by international law.

A cardinal principle which resides hand in hand with the *"harm prevention"* principle is the principle of *pollution prevention*. This principle is enshrined in Article 3 of the Draft Articles on the Prevention of Transboundary Harm from Hazardous Activities of the International Law Commission which states:

> States shall take all appropriate measures to prevent significant transboundary harm or at any event, to minimize the risk thereof.

This is essentially a preventive principle which calls for States to anticipate environmental damage and to act prospectively to avoid or prevent such damage.

Another important principle of environmental law is the *Precautionary Principle*. Essentially, the precautionary Principle addresses ways and means to make decisions prospectively in the face of environmental uncertainty or when possible threats are posed to society.

The Stockholm Declaration of 1972 also brought to bear the fact that the protection and improvement of the human environment is a major issue which affects the well-being of peoples and economic development throughout the world; and therefore it was the urgent desire of the peoples of the whole world and the duty of all Governments. It also highlighted the fundamental cause of environmental pollution by focussing on the fact that in the developing countries in particular, most of the environmental problems are caused by under-development. Furthermore, the Declaration recognized that millions continue to live far below the minimum levels required for a decent human existence, deprived of adequate food and clothing, shelter and education, health and sanitation. Therefore, the developing countries must direct their efforts to development, bearing in mind their priorities and the need to safeguard and improve the environment. The Declaration went on to assert that, for the same purpose, the industrialized countries should make efforts to reduce the gap themselves and the developing countries. The basic issue was that in the industrialized countries, environmental problems are generally related to industrialization and technological development.

Arguably the three most important principles of the Stockholm Declaration were firstly, that the natural resources of the earth, including the air, water, land, flora and fauna and especially representative samples of natural ecosystems, must be safeguarded for the benefit of present and future generations through careful planning or management, as appropriate. Secondly, the capacity of the earth to produce vital renewable resources must be maintained and, wherever practicable, restored or improved. Thirdly, the Declaration was explicit in Principle Six that the discharge of toxic substances or of other substances and the release of heat, in such quantities or concentrations as to exceed the capacity of the environment to render them harmless, must be halted in order to ensure that serious or irreversible damage is not inflicted upon ecosystems. The just struggle of the peoples of ill countries against pollution should be supported. Principle Twelve went on to say that resources should be made available to preserve and improve the environment, taking into account the circumstances and particular requirements of developing countries and any costs which may emanate from their incorporating environmental safeguards into their development planning and the need for making available to them, upon their request, additional international technical and financial assistance for this purpose.

These principles formed both the genesis of and precursor to action on environmental protection. The Rio Conference on Environment and Development[11] which took place in 1992 was another landmark in global legislative and regulatory initiative. This Conference, which will be referred to later in this book, adopted the Rio Declaration which, while endorsing the Stockholm Declaration and its principles stated that, in order to achieve sustainable development, environmental protection shall constitute an integral part of the development process and cannot be considered in isolation from it. The Declaration, in Principle Seven states that States shall cooperate in a spirit of global partnership to conserve, protect and restore the health and integrity of the Earth's ecosystem. In view of the different contributions to global environmental degradation, States have common but differentiated responsibilities. By adopting the Rio Declaration, the developed countries acknowledged the responsibility that they bear in the international pursuit to sustainable development in view of the pressures their societies place on the global environment and of the technologies and financial resources they command. The Declaration also called for global and consensual efforts at environmental protection, stating inter alia in Principle Twelve that unilateral actions to deal with environmental challenges outside the jurisdiction of the importing country should be avoided. Environmental measures addressing transboundary or global environmental problems should, as far as possible, be based on an international consensus. From an aviation context, as will be seen in later discussions on aircraft engine emissions, the principle of consensus enunciated in Principle Twelve has become a contentious issue, particularly on the subject of emissions trading.

---

[11] United Nations Conference on Environment and Development (UNCED) held in Rio de Janerio, Brazil, 3–14 June 1992 See UN Doc.A/CONF.151/26, reprinted in 31 *ILM* 874 (1992). It must be mentioned that in the 1980s the UN set up the World Commission on Environment and Development, also called the Brundtland Commission. They produced "*Our Common Future*", otherwise known as the Brundtland Report, which framed much of what would become the 40 chapters of Agenda 21 and the 27 principles of the Rio Declaration on Environment and Development. It defined sustainable development as development which; "*meets the needs of present generations without compromising the ability of future generations to meet their own needs*".

At the Earth Summit in Rio, the international community adopted Agenda 21, an unprecedented global plan of action for sustainable development. Agenda 21 which was adopted by more than 178 Governments at the Rio Summit, is a comprehensive plan of action to be taken globally, nationally and locally by organizations of the United Nations System, Governments, and major groups in every area in which the human impact on the environment. Part of Agenda 21 was to establish the United Nations Commission on Sustainable Development (CSD)[12] which was created in December 1992 to ensure effective follow-up of the Rio Conference to monitor and report on implementation of the agreements at the local, national, regional and international levels.

The World Summit on Sustainable Development (WSSD) held in Johannesburg, South Africa from 26 August to 4 September 2002 strongly reaffirmed and endorsed the full implementation of Agenda 21, the Programme for Further Implementation of Agenda 21 and the Commitments to the Rio principles. It was in essence a clarion call to the world to endorse and adhere to the earlier Declarations. It could be said that one of the signal contributions of the Johannesburg Summit was that it acted as the precursor to a link between human rights law and environmental law. Sumudu Atapattu,[13] a renowned environmental law scholar and professor at the University of Wisconsin is of the view that this link is most commonly seen in South Asia. She cites the right to health and the right to adequate standards of living as economic and social rights that touch on environmental issues.

Access to information is also a right enshrined in the general principles of environmental law. Principle 10 of the Rio Declaration states inter alia that at the national level, each individual is entitled to have appropriate access to information concerning the environment that is held by public authorities, including information of hazardous materials and activities in their communities, and the opportunity to participate in the decision making processes. This abundantly shows that good governance is an integral element and critical requirement in the environmental process of a country and is a facilitator in achieving sustainable development.

---

[12] The United Nations Commission on Sustainable Development (CSD) was established by the UN General Assembly in December 1992 to ensure effective follow-up of United Nations Conference on Environment and Development UNCED, also known as the Earth Summit. The Commission is responsible for reviewing progress in the implementation of Agenda 21 and the Rio Declaration; as well as providing policy guidance to follow up the Johannesburg Plan of Implementation (JPOI) at the local, national, regional and international levels. The JPOI reaffirmed that the CSD is the high-level forum for sustainable development within the United Nations system.

[13] Atapattu, *supra*, note 50 at 9.

The UN Framework Convention on Climate Change (UNFCC)

In 1990, the Inter Governmental Panel on Climate Change (IPCC)[14] put forward the suggestion that there should be a framework convention on climate change along the lines of the Vienna Convention on the Depletion of the Ozone Layer.[15] In 1992, at the Earth Summit in Rio de Janeiro, the UNFCC, a treaty intended to achieve stabilization of greenhouse gas concentrations in the atmosphere at a level that would prevent dangerous anthropogenic interference with the climate system. The objective of UNFCC, as reflected in Article 2 is to achieve, in accordance with the relevant provisions of the Convention, stabilization of greenhouse gas concentrations in the atmosphere at a level that would prevent dangerous anthropogenic interference with the climate system. The Convention goes on to say that such a level should be achieved within a time-frame sufficient to allow ecosystems to adapt naturally to climate change, to ensure that food production is not threatened and to enable economic development to proceed in a sustainable manner. The basic principles of the Convention call for State Parties to protect the climate

---

[14] The IPCC is a scientific intergovernmental body set up by the World Meteorological Organization (WMO) and by the United Nations Environment Programme (UNEP). The IPCC was established to provide the decision-makers and others interested in climate change with an objective source of information about climate change. The IPCC does not conduct any research nor does it monitor climate related data or parameters. Its role is to assess on a comprehensive, objective, open and transparent basis the latest scientific, technical and socio-economic literature produced worldwide relevant to the understanding of the risk of human-induced climate change, its observed and projected impacts and options for adaptation and mitigation. IPCC reports should be neutral with respect to policy, although they need to deal objectively with policy relevant scientific, technical and socio economic factors. They should be of high scientific and technical standards, and aim to reflect a range of views, expertise and wide geographical coverage.

[15] The Vienna Convention for the Protection of the Ozone Layer (1985) outlines States' responsibilities for protecting human health and the environment against the adverse effects of ozone depletion, establishes the framework under which the Montreal Protocol was negotiated, created a general obligation for nations to take appropriate measures to protect the ozone layer and a process by which regulations could be created by the governments of countries to establish control measures. The Convention also established a mechanism for international cooperation in research, monitoring, and exchange of data on the state of the stratospheric ozone layer and on emissions and concentrations of CFCs and other relevant chemicals. Most importantly, the Vienna Convention established the framework for a future protocol—the Montreal Protocol on Substances that Deplete the Ozone Layer. The Montreal Protocol on Substances that Deplete the Ozone Layer is a landmark international agreement designed to protect the stratospheric ozone layer. The treaty was originally signed in 1987 and substantially amended in 1990 and 1992. The Montreal Protocol stipulates that the production and consumption of compounds that deplete ozone in the stratosphere—chlorofluorocarbons (CFCs), halons, carbon tetrachloride, and methyl chloroform—are to be phased out by 2000 (2005 for methyl chloroform). Scientific theory and evidence suggest that, once emitted to the atmosphere, these compounds could significantly deplete the stratospheric ozone layer that shields the planet from damaging UV-B radiation. The United Nations Environment Programme (UNEP) has prepared a Montreal Protocol Handbook that provides additional detail and explanation of the provisions.

system for the benefit of present and future generations of humankind, on the basis of equity and in accordance with their common but differentiated responsibilities and respective capabilities. Accordingly, it calls for the developed country Parties to take the lead in combating climate change and its adverse effects.

UNFCC also calls for consideration to be given to the specific needs and special circumstances of developing country Parties, especially those that are particularly vulnerable to the adverse effects of climate change, and of those Parties, especially developing country Parties, that would have to bear a disproportionate or abnormal burden under the Convention.

Furthermore in Article 3 UNFCC calls for Parties to take precautionary measures to anticipate, prevent or minimize the causes of climate change and mitigate its adverse effects. Where there are threats of serious or irreversible damage, lack of full scientific certainty should not be used as a reason for postponing such measures, taking into account that policies and measures to deal with climate change should be cost-effective so as to ensure global benefits at the lowest possible cost. To achieve this, the Convention prescribes that such policies and measures should take into account different socio-economic contexts, be comprehensive, cover all relevant sources, sinks and reservoirs of greenhouse gases and adaptation, and comprise all economic sectors. There is also the suggestion that efforts to address climate change may be carried out cooperatively by interested Parties.

Under the Convention, the Parties have a right to, and should, promote sustainable development. Policies and measures to protect the climate system against human-induced change should be appropriate for the specific conditions of each Party and should be integrated with national development programmes, taking into account that economic development is essential for adopting measures to address climate change.

State Parties are required to cooperate to promote a supportive and open international economic system that would lead to sustainable economic growth and development in all Parties, particularly developing country Parties, thus enabling them better to address the problems of climate change. There is also the prescription that measures taken to combat climate change, including unilateral ones, should not constitute a means of arbitrary or unjustifiable discrimination or a disguised restriction on international trade.

Article 17 stipulates inter alia that the Conference of the Parties may, at any ordinary session, adopt protocols to the Convention and that only Parties to the Convention may be Parties to a protocol. The Kyoto Protocol, an Amendment to UNFCC agreed upon in 1997, is a product of this provision. Noteworthy among the Protocol's contents is Annex 1 which commits 36 of the Annexe's Parties (known as Annex B Parties) to individual targets for limiting or reducing emissions which, taken together, would reduce overall emissions of six greenhouse gases from these countries by approximately 5 per cent below 1990 levels within the Protocol's first commitment period—2008 to 2012. The Kyoto Protocol therefore establishes legally binding commitments for the reduction of six greenhouse gases, carbon dioxide; methane; nitrous oxide, sulphur hexachloride;

hydroflourocarbons and perflourocarbons produced by industrialized nations identified in Annex 1 to the Protocol and prescribes general commitments for all member countries. The Protocol, which was initially adopted for use on 11 December 1997 in Kyoto, Japan, entered into force on 16 February 2005. Under this Protocol, industrialized countries agreed to reduce their collective greenhouse gas emissions by 5.2 % compared to the year 1990. National limitations range from 8 % reductions for the European Union and some others, to 7 % for the United States, 6 % for Japan, and 0 % for Russia. The treaty permitted greenhouse gas emission increases of 8 % for Australia and 10 % for Iceland.

Some mechanisms suggested by the Kyoto Protocol include those that are termed "flexible mechanisms" such as emissions trading, the clean development mechanism and joint implementation with a view to allowing Annex I economies to meet their greenhouse gas emission limitations by purchasing emission reductions credits from elsewhere, through financial exchanges, projects that reduce emissions in non-Annex I economies, from other Annex I countries, or from Annex I countries with excess allowances. In practice this means that Non-Annex I economies have no greenhouse gas emission restrictions, but have financial incentives to develop greenhouse gas emission reduction projects to receive carbon credits that can then be sold to Annex I buyers. It is believed that this trading practice would promote and encourage sustainable development, encouraging In addition, the flexible mechanisms allow Annex I nations with efficient, low greenhouse gas-emitting industries, and high prevailing environmental standards to purchase carbon credits on the world market instead of reducing greenhouse gas emissions domestically. Annex I entities typically will want to acquire carbon credits as cheaply as possible, while Non-Annex I entities want to maximize the value of carbon credits generated from their domestic Greenhouse Gas Projects.

Designated national authorities have been established by all signatories to Annex I signatories and the mandate of these authorities is to manage their greenhouse gas portfolios. Most of the non-Annex I countries have also established such authorities to manage the Kyoto process, specifically the clean development mechanism process that determines which greenhouse gas projects they wish to propose for accreditation by the clean development mechanism executive board.

The Kyoto Protocol has assigned ICAO the task of reducing the impact of aircraft engine emissions, but so far the Organization has resisted measures that would impose mandatory fuel taxes or emissions standards. In 2001, the 35th ICAO Assembly urged its member states to develop the means to limit the environmental impact of aircraft emissions, and requested that ICAO's governing body work with the United Nations Framework Convention on Climate Change to develop policy options for reducing aircraft emissions.

Evolution of Aviation Environmental Law and Regulation

The Chicago Convention[16] is the fundamental source which grants regulatory powers to the international community on matters relating to international civil aviation. The Convention in its Preamble proclaims that the governments that are parties to it agree on certain principles and arrangements in order that international civil aviation may be developed in a safe and orderly manner. Public safety is a feature of major concern to the Convention which requires that:

> Each contracting State may, for reasons of military necessity or public safety, restrict or prohibit uniformly the aircraft of other States from flying over certain areas of its territory… Such prohibited areas shall be of reasonable extent and location so as not to interfere unnecessarily with air navigation. Descriptions of such prohibited areas in the territory of a contracting State, as well as any subsequent alterations therein, shall be communicated as soon as possible to the other contracting States and to the International Civil Aviation Organization.[17]

The Convention also established the International Civil Aviation Organization which is required as one of its objectives to foster the planning and development of international air transport so as inter alia to ensure the safe and orderly growth of international civil aviation throughout the world,[18] meet the needs of the people of the world for safe, regular, efficient and economic air transport,[19] promote safety of flight in international air navigation,[20] and promote generally the development of all aspects of international civil aviation.[21] To this end, ICAO is mandated by the Convention to adopt and amend from time to time as may be necessary, international Standards and Recommended Practices and Procedures (SARPS) dealing inter alia with characteristics of airports and landing areas and such matters concerned with the safety, regularity and efficiency of air navigation as may from time to time be appropriate.[22] Each contracting State has undertaken to collaborate in securing the highest practicable degree of uniformity in the above regulations, standards and procedures of the Organization.

There is no argument that the principles of environmental law pertaining to aviation would attenuate the general principles discussed above, as they evolved through the three Declarations and the judicial pronouncements. However, the regulatory process with regard to aviation environmental law started with the international civil aviation organization. ICAO's initiatives at environmental protection commenced o 2 April 1971 (even prior to the Stockholm Conference)

---

[16] Convention on International Civil Aviation, signed at Chicago on 7 December 1944, ICAO Doc 7300./9: 2006.

[17] Article 9.

[18] Article 44(a).

[19] Article 44(d).

[20] Article 44(n).

[21] Article 44(i).

[22] Article 37(b).

when the Organization adopted Standards and Recommended Practices to Annex 16 to the Chicago Convention on the subject of aircraft noise. The work on developing the Annex started in ICAO as far back as in 1968 when the sixteenth session of the ICAO Assembly adopted Resolution A16-3 which recognized the burgeoning problem of aircraft noise in the vicinity of airports and called for global action to alleviate the inconvenience caused to residents near airports.

ICAO's regulatory role in aircraft engine emissions is enshrined in Volume II of Annex 16 and is historically linked to the 1972 United Nations Conference on the Human Environment which was held in Stockholm. The position of ICAO at this Conference was developed in Assembly Resolution A18-11 which contained the following clause among others:

in fulfilling this role ICAO is conscious of the adverse environmental impact that may be related to aircraft activity and its responsibility and that of its member States to achieve maximum compatibility between "the safe and orderly development of civil aviation and the quality of the human environment;"

The 18th Assembly also adopted Resolution A18-12 relating to the environment which stated:

"The Assembly:

Requests the Council, with the assistance and co-operation of other bodies of the Organization and other international organizations to continue with vigour the work related to the development of Standards, Recommended Practices and Procedures and/or guidance material dealing with the quality of the human environment;"

This resolution was followed up by the establishment of an ICAO Action Programme Regarding the Environment. As part of this Action Programme a Study Group was established to assist the Secretariat in certain tasks related to aircraft engine emissions. As a result of the work of this Study Group, an ICAO Circular entitled *Control of Aircraft Engine Emissions* (Circular 134-AN/94) was published in 1977. This Circular contained guidance material in the form of a certification procedure for the control of vented fuel, smoke and certain gaseous emissions for new turbojet and turbofan engines intended for propulsion at subsonic speeds.

It was agreed by the Council that the subject of aircraft engine emissions was not one that was solely confined to objective technical issues but was one that needed consideration by experts in many fields and included the direct views of Member States. A Council committee, known as the Committee on Aircraft Engine Emissions (CAEE) was therefore established in 1977 to pursue a number of aspects of the subject.

At the second meeting of the Committee on Aircraft Engine Emissions, held in May 1980, proposals were made for material to be included in an ICAO Annex. After amendment following the usual consultation with Member States of the Organization, the proposed material was adopted by the Council to form the text of this document. The Council agreed that it was desirable to include all provisions relating to environmental aspects of aviation in one Annex. It therefore retained the title of Annex 16 as "Environmental Protection", making the existing text of the Annex into "Volume I—Aircraft Noise", and "Volume 2—Aircraft Engine Emissions".

Part I of Volume 2 of Annex 16 contains definitions and symbols and Part II contains Standards relating to vented fuel. Part III contains Standards relating to emissions certification applicable to the classes of aircraft engines specified in the individual chapters of the Part, where such engines are fitted to aircraft engaged in international civil aviation.

The balancing of airport development and ecological considerations i.e. city planning, noise pollution avoidance, is also very much a part of ICAO's regulatory role in issues related to the effects of international civil aviation on the environment. The ICAO *Airport Planning Manual*[23] ensures a balance between airport development and ecological considerations and includes findings of ICAO on aviation and the environment.

In its findings, ICAO records that studies of air quality at certain large airports and nearby areas reflect the fact that automobiles, airport ground vehicles and other urban pollution sources account for most of the atmospheric pollution[24] and that airports may destroy the natural habitat and feeding grounds of wild life and may eradicate or deplete certain flora important to the ecological balance of the area.[25] The Manual also considers the necessity to avoid contamination of rivers and streams by airport waste disposal and drainage systems,[26] the avoidance of noise caused by aircraft to human habitation[27] and highway planning.[28] Finally, the document calls for a detailed study of the impact of airport development on the environment in the form of an environmental impact statement.[29]

The ICAO Assembly has, in addition, adopted several Resolutions concerning aviation and the environment. At its 22nd Assembly held in September/October 1977 the ICAO Assembly adopted Resolution A22-12 which recognized inter alia the following:

(1) advancing technology has caused aviation to become a significant influence in the environment;

(2) many of the adverse environmental effects of civil aviation activity can be reduced by, the application of integrated measures embracing technological improvements, appropriate noise abatement operating procedures, proper organization of air traffic and the appropriate use of airport planning and land use control mechanisms;

(3) other international organizations are becoming involved in activities relating to noise abatement policies;

---

[23] See *Airport Planning Manual* Doc 9184—AN 902 Part 2, 13.2.

[24] Id. 2.1.3.

[25] Id. 2.2.1.

[26] Id. 2.4.1.

[27] Id. 2.5.2.

[28] Id. 4.3.1.

[29] Id. 2.6.1.

(4) in fulfilling its role, ICAO strives to achieve a balance between the benefit of accruing to the world community through civil aviation and the harm caused to the human environment in certain areas through the progressive advancement of civil aviation;

The Assembly therefore declared:

(1) that ICAO is conscious of the adverse environmental impacts that may be related to aircraft activity and of its responsibility and that of its Contracting States to achieve maximum compatibility between the safe and orderly development of civil aviation and the quality of the human environment;
(2) that the Council Should maintain its vigilance in the pursuit of aviation interests related to the human environment and also maintain the initiative in developing policy guidance on all aviation matters related to the human environment, and not leave such initiatives to other organizations;

The Assembly also invited States to continue their active support for ICAO's Action Programme Regarding the Environment on all appropriate occasions as their participation in civil aviation's contribution to the United Nations Environment Programme (UNEP) and authorised the ICAO Council, if and when it deems this desirable, to enter into cooperative arrangements with the United Nations Environment Programme for the execution of environmental projects financed by the United Nations Environment Fund. The Assembly urged States to refrain from unilateral measures that would be harmful to the development of international civil aviation.

At the same Session, the Assembly adopted Resolution A22-13 on airports and the environment, observing inter alia:

(1) the compatibility between the airport and its environment was one of the elements to be taken into account in long-term systems planning;
(2) the problem of aircraft noise in the vicinity of many of the world's airports continued to arouse public concern and required appropriate action;
(3) the introduction of future aircraft types could increase and aggravate this noise unless action was taken to alleviate the situation.

The Assembly therefore requested the council to continue its work on establishing Standards and Recommended Practices relating to the alleviation of the problem and urged contracting States to adopt, where appropriate, the ICAO measures and procedures applicable.

In the following Session (September/October 1980), the Assembly adopted Resolution A23-10 on aircraft noise and engine emissions from subsonic aircraft and requested contracting States not to allow the operation of foreign registered subsonic jet planes that did not conform to ICAO's specifications on noise certification standards as specified in Annex 16 until 1 January 1988.[30] At the 28th Assembly Sessions held in October 1990, the ICAO Assembly observed that while

---

[30] See *Assembly Resolutions in Force* (as of 6 October 1989), *ICAO Doc 9558* at II-18.

certification standards for subsonic jet aircraft noise levels are specified in Volume 1, Chaps. 2 and 3 of Annex 16 and that environmental problems due to aircraft noise continued to exist in the neighbourhood of many international airports, some States were consequently considering restrictions on the operations of aircraft which exceed the noise levels in Volume I, Chap. 3 of Annex 16. The Assembly also recognized that the noise standards in Annex 16 were not intended to introduce operating restrictions on aircraft and that operating restrictions on existing aircraft would increase the costs of airlines and would impose a heavy economic burden, particularly on those airlines which do not have the financial resources to re-equip their fleets. Therefore, considering that resolution of problems due to aircraft noise must be based on the mutual recognition of the difficulties encountered by States and a balance among their different concerns, the Assembly, by Resolution A28-3, urged States not to introduce any new operating restrictions on aircraft which exceed the noise levels in Volume I, Chap. 3 of Annex 16 before considering:

(a) whether the normal attrition of existing fleets of such aircraft will provide the necessary protection of noise climates around their airports;
(b) whether the necessary protection can be achieved by regulations preventing their operators from adding such aircraft to their fleets through either purchase, or lease/charter/interchange, or alternatively by incentives to accelerate fleet modernization;
(c) whether the necessary protection can be achieved through restrictions limited to airports and runways the use of which has been identified and declared by them as generating noise problems and limited to time periods when greater noise disturbance is caused; and,
(d) the implications of any restrictions for other States concerned, consulting these States and giving them reasonable notice of intention

The Assembly further urged States:

(a) to frame any restrictions so that Chap. 2 compliant aircraft of an individual operator which are presently operating to their territories may be withdrawn from these operations gradually over a period of not less than 7 years;
(b) not to begin the above phase-in period for any restrictions before 1 April 1995;
(c) not to restrict before the end of the phase-in period the operations of any aircraft less than 25 years after the date of issue of its first individual certificate of airworthiness;
(d) not to restrict before the end of the phase-in period the operations of any presently existing wide-body aircraft or of any fitted with high by-pass ratio engines;
(e) to apply any restrictions consistently with the non-discrimination principle in Article 15 of the Chicago Convention so as to give foreign operators at least as favourable treatment as their own operators at the same airports; and,
(f) to inform ICAO, as well as the other States concerned, of all restrictions imposed.

The Assembly also strongly encouraged States to continue to cooperate bilaterally, regionally and inter-regionally with a view to:

(a) alleviating the noise burden on communities around airports without imposing severe economic hardship on aircraft operators; and

(b) taking into account the problems of operators of developing countries with regard to Chap. 2 aircraft presently on their register, where they cannot be replaced before the end of the phase-in period, provided that there is proof of a purchase order or leasing contract placed for a replacement Chap. 3 compliant aircraft and the first date of delivery of the aircraft has been accepted;

The Assembly, while urging States, if and when any new noise certification standards are introduced which are more stringent than those in Volume I, Chap. 3 of Annex 16, not to impose any operating restrictions on Chap. 3 compliant aircraft, urged the Council to promote and States to develop an integrated approach to the problem of aircraft noise, including land-use planning procedures around international airports, so that any residential, industrial or other land-use that might be adversely affected by aircraft noise is minimal. The Assembly further urged States to assist aircraft operators in their efforts to accelerate fleet modernization and thereby prevent obstacles and permit all States to have access to lease or purchase aircraft compliant with Chap. 3, including the provision of multilateral technical assistance where appropriate. This Resolution superseded Resolution A23-10, which was discussed above.

Resolution A28-3 represents a cautious balance between the concerns of the aircraft manufacturers, the airline industry and developing States who do not wish to lose in the near future, the services of Chap. 2 aircraft which are already in use and service. Although aircraft manufactured prior to October 1977 that are included in Chap. 2 of Annex 16 and called "Chap. 2 aircraft" are required to be phased out, the compromise in Resolution A28-3 allows States that have noise problems at airports to start phasing out operations by Chap. 2 aircraft from the year 1995 and to have all of them withdrawn by the year 2002, with some exceptions. The Resolution envisages that by the year 2002 only aircraft manufactured after October 1977 and described in Chap. 3 of Annex 16 (called "Chap. 3 aircraft) would be in operation. Following this resolution, a number of developed States have already started to phase out Chap. 2 aircraft, while giving due recognition to the compromise reached in Resolution A28-3.

In order to carry out its policies in environmental issues related to civil aviation, ICAO established the Committee on Environmental Protection (CAEP) in 1983.[31] The CAEP is a technical committee reporting to the ICAO Council and consisting of 14 members nominated by their States. The members are experts in the field of aviation and the environment. One of the CAEPs positive contributions to ICAO's environmental programme has been the development of a new chapter for Volume 1 of Annex 16, which contains a noise certification scheme for light helicopters as

---

[31] For more details on CAEP see Mortimer (1992).

well as a number of modifications to the technical specifications of the Annex. The CAEP believes that although ICAO initiatives on Chap. 2 aircraft withdrawal will ameliorate the problem of noise near airports, it will be short lived, as the rapidly increasing proportions of international air travel in the next few years will render the benefits brought about by the initiative, nugatory.

ICAO's active involvement in aviation related environmental issues is not without good reason, as 9 of the 27 principles contained in the Declaration of the United Nations Conference on Environment and Development (UNCED)—also known as the "Earth Summit"—held in Rio de Janeiro in June 1992. They are:

1. "States have... the responsibility to ensure that activities within their jurisdiction or control do not cause damage to the environment of other States or of areas beyond the limits of national jurisdiction." (Principle 2).
2. "The special situation and needs of developing countries, particularly the least developed... shall be given special priority. International actions in the field of environment and development should also address the interests and needs of all countries." (Principle 6).
3. "In view of the different contributions to global environmental degradation, States have common but differentiated responsibilities. The developed countries acknowledge the responsibility that they bear in the international pursuit of sustainable development in view of the pressures their societies place on the global environment and of the technologies and financial resources they command." (Principle 7).
4. "To achieve sustainable development and a higher quality of life for all people, States should reduce and eliminate unsustainable patterns of production and consumption..." (Principle 8).
5. "States shall enact effective environmental legislation. Environmental standards, management objectives and priorities should reflect the environmental and developmental context to which they apply. Standards applied by some countries may be inappropriate and of unwarranted economic and social cost to other countries, in particular developing countries." (Principle 11).
6. Environmental measures addressing transboundary or global environmental problems should, as far as possible, be based on an international consensus." (Principle 12).
7. "In order to protect the environment, the precautionary approach shall be widely applied by States according to their capabilities. Where there are threats of serious or irreversible damage, lack of full scientific certainty shall not be used as a reason for postponing cost-effective measures to prevent environmental degradation." (Principle 15).
8. "National authorities should endeavour to promote the internalization of environmental costs and the use of economic instruments, taking into account the approach that the polluter should, in principle, bear the cost of pollution,..." (Principle 16).

9. "Environmental impact assessment, as a national instrument, shall be under-taken for proposed activities that are likely to have a significant adverse impact on the environment and are subject to a decision of a competent national authority." (Principle 17).

ICAO has reached the cross roads of development in air transport where air traffic growth, which is exponential, has to keep pace with sustainable development. Current trends therefore call for much harmonization through global cooperation so as to ensure that air transport development and sustainable development go hand in hand. ICAO works in close harmony with other specialized agencies of the United Nations and with international organizations such as the International Air Transport Association (which represents airlines) and Airports Council International which is the international body representing the airports of the world. ICAO is driven by its own Business Plan which has, as one of its strategic objectives to minimize the adverse effects of aviation on the environment. Broadly ICAO aims to achieve this objective by minimizing the adverse environmental effects of global civil aviation activity, notably aircraft noise and aircraft engine emissions, through the following measures: develop, adopt and promote new or amended measures to limit or reduce the number of people affected by significant aircraft noise; limit or reduce the impact of aircraft engine emissions on local air quality; and limit or reduce the impact of aviation greenhouse gas emissions on the global climate. Another ICAO aim in this regard is to cooperate with other international bodies and in particular the UN Framework Convention on Climate Change (UNFCCC) in addressing aviation's contribution to global climate change.

As was earlier stated, the primary responsibility of global regulatory control of aviation and the environment rests with ICAO, which has been working in this area since 1968. ICAO's work is tied in with various international conferences that have been held over the past 15 years. These conferences, and ICAO's own conscious awareness of the need ti protect aviation from the deleterious effects of greenhouse gases have brought to bear an awareness of the meaning and purpose of sustainable aviation development in the Organization.

Essentially, the term "sustainable development" in the context of environ-mental protection means "development which the environment can sustain without being polluted". It essentially conveys the message that the present generation should develop the world without compromising the potential of future generations to keep the development process going in an unpolluted environment. The term has its genesis in the *Rio Summit* which had the following priorities incorporated in its Report, in Agenda 21:

(1) achieving sustainable growth, as through integrating environment and development in decision-making;
(2) fostering an equitable world, as by combating poverty and protecting human health;
(3) making the world habitable by addressing issues of urban water supply, solid waste management, and urban pollution;

(4) encouraging efficient resource use, a category which includes management of energy resources, care and use of fresh water, forest development, management of fragile eco systems, conservation of biological diversity, and management of land resources;

(5) protecting global and regional resources, including the atmosphere, oceans and seas, and living marine resources; and

(6) managing chemicals and hazardous and nuclear wastes.

For the above purposes, member States of the United Nations agreed at the Conference to establish a new Commission for Sustainable Development which was mandated to monitor and review the implementation of Agenda 21. The UNCED initiative re-established the notion that environment is an inextricable and integral part of sustainable development and that environmental issues were not sui generis or stand-alone issues but were incontrovertibly linked to their economic, political and social contexts. The general thrust of the UNCED conclusions was that environmental issues were the necessary corollaries to social processes and should be addressed on the basis of equity, care for nature and natural resources and development of society.

Environmental management is therefore the key to effective sustainable development. The flavour of the UNCED process introduced a hitherto unknown element in environmental protection—a diversion from the mere cleaning up or repairing damage to being a sustained social activity which brings to bear the need to force development to keep pace with the environmental equilibrium and stability of the world.

Another integral part of sustainable development is economics. Economics not only plays a key role in societal decision-making, but it also integrates environmental issues with distribution, ownership and control, identifying economic development and social issues as major elements in the management of a society. Another aspect of the role of economics in sustainable development is reflected in the very nature of sustainable development itself, in that it requires a delicate balance between the needs of the present generation and the long-term environmental well being of a society. If, for instance, the alienation of environmental assets which enrich the present generation, but would adversely affect future generations, the management of this dichotomy could be addressed by considering primarily, the economic implications of unsustainable development.

Another factor which influences sustainable development is globalization, which calls for intervention at international level to ensure that development could be sustained environmentally. In this context, in addition to the implementation of international environmental agreements, it becomes necessary to critically analyze the impact of the global economy and the liberalization of trade on environmental issues.

The UNCED process epitomizes the premise that any bifurcation of environment and sustainable development is arbitrary and cosmetic. With this in view, sustainable development is now internationally managed by the primary United Nations regulatory body on the environment—the United Nations Environmental Programme (UNEP)—which addresses the subject of sustainable development in three component elements:

(i) environmental assessment: through the evaluation and review, research and monitoring and the exchange of views on the environment;
(ii) environmental management: through comprehensive planning that takes into account the effects of the acts of humans on the environment; and
(iii) supporting measures: through education, training and public information and also through financial assistance and organizational arrangements.

The above tools are used by UNEP in carrying out the task assigned to it by Agenda 21 of UNCED, which, in its Chap. 38, paragraph 22 set out the following priority areas on which UNEP should concentrate on:

a. Strengthening its catalytic role in stimulating and promoting environmental activities and considerations throughout the United Nations system;
b. Promoting international co-operation in the field of environment and recommending, as appropriate, policies to this end; Developing and promoting the use of techniques such as natural resource accounting and environmental economics;
c. Environmental monitoring and assessment, both through improved participation by the United Nations system agencies in the Earthwatch programme and expanded relations with private scientific and non-governmental research institutes; strengthening and making operational its early-warning function;
d. Co-ordination and promotion of relevant scientific research with a view to providing a consolidated basis for decision-making;
e. Dissemination of environmental information and data to Governments and to organs, programmes and organizations of the United Nations system;
f. Raising general awareness and action in the area of environmental protection through collaboration with the general public, non-governmental entities and intergovernmental institutions;
g. Further development of international environmental law, in particular conventions and guidelines, promotion of its implementation, and co-ordinating functions arising from an increasing number of international legal agreements, inter alia, the functioning of the secretariats of the Conventions, taking into account the need for the most efficient use of resources, including possible co-location of secretariats established in the future;
h. Further development and promotion of the widest possible use of environmental impact assessments, including activities carried out under the auspices of specialized agencies of the United Nations system, and in connection with every significant economic development project or activity.
i. Facilitation of information exchange on environmentally sound technologies, including legal aspects, and provision of training;
j. Promotion of sub-regional and regional co-operation and support to relevant initiatives and programmes for environmental protection, including playing a major contributing and co-ordinating role in the regional mechanisms in the field of environment identified for the follow-up to the Conference;
k. Provision of technical, legal and institutional advice to Governments, upon request, in establishing and enhancing their national legal and institutional frameworks, in particular, in co-operation with UNDP capacity-building efforts;

l. Support to Governments, upon request, and development agencies and organs in the integration of environmental aspects into their developmental policies and programmes, in particular through provision of environmental, technical and policy advice during programme formulation and implementation;

m. Further developing assessment and assistance in cases of environmental emergencies.

In addition to Chap. 38, directives are specifically given to UNEP or to UNEP in collaboration with others, in sixteen chapters of Agenda 21. Agenda 21 was endorsed by United Nations General Assembly resolution 47/19 of 22 December 1992.

The expectations placed upon and the tasks assigned to UNEP by the international community thus confirm UNEP's approach of positioning the environment in the broader context of sustainable development. UNEP's mandate is consistent with the conclusion that the environment cannot be viewed in isolation and needs to be managed within the integrated context of sustainable development. This approach was confirmed by the global community at UNCED.

Although UNEP's role is clearly set out, it is somewhat obfuscated by the perceived overlap between the UNEP and another United Nations body—the Commission on Sustainable Development (CSD) both of which are involved—within the parameters of Agenda 21 of UNCED—in issues addressing environment and development. The CSD is ineluctably involved in Agenda 21, of which the main thrust is sustainable development. Sustainable development in turn is linked to environmental and developmental issues, which is identified with the scope of work which UNEP is involved in. However, this seemingly obvious duplication is not an absolute one since UNEP's main interest lies in the environment, whereas the CSD focuses primarily on sustainable development. However, the scope and functions of the CSD, as reflected in Agenda 21, although bordering largely on monitoring and review, also involves for the CSD a largely interactive role with organizational and governmental entities which are involved with the implementation of Agenda 21. This function irrevocably overlaps with that of the UNEP and may therefore be considered by the world at large as a perceived duplication. Another area of potential overlap between the two bodies lies in the existence of the Department for Policy Co-ordination on Sustainable Development (DPCSD) which provides support for the CSD and therefore is involved in the same work as UNEP. The UNEP and CSD dichotomy is also seen in their roles in monitoring progress made by the international Community under international conventions. Be that as it may, both bodies have so far performed their functions without tangible duplication, while contributing to Agenda 21 positively.[32]

The United Nations Inter-Agency Committee on Sustainable Development (IACSD) is yet another body which addresses the subject of sustainable development within the United Nations umbrella. The IACSD was established by the

---

[32] UNEP/GC.18/27, 21 March 1995.

Administrative Committee on Co-ordination (ACC) which was set up under
Agenda 21. The ACC, which was charged with ensuring the smooth and effective
implementation of Agenda 21, in turn established the IACSD which identifies
major policy issues under UNCED and advises the ACC on ways and means of
addressing them. In addition, the IACSD identifies overall policy issues for the
ACC under its guidance and advises ACC of major lapses and constraints affecting
the United Nations system in the UNCED follow up.[33]

The Johannesburg Summit

The main objective of the World Summit on Sustainable Development, which was
held in Johannesburg from 26 August to 4 September 2002, was to hold a 10 years
review of the Rio Summit in order to re-energize the existing global commitment to
sustainable developmen. The deliberations of the Johannesburg Summit resulted in
the adoption of two documents i.e. the *Johannesburg Declaratio* (the Declaration)[34]
and the *Plan of Implementatio* The Declaration, while drawing on the rich history of
global environmental protection measures, reconfirmed the world's commitment to
sustainable development through multilateral solution seeking and implementation.
The three fundamental foundations of sustainable development, as endorsed by the
Declaration, are poverty eradication, change of consumption and production patterns and protection and management of the natural resource base. Of these, consumption, production and protection of nature are critical for air transport and in
this context The *Plan of Implementation's* recognition of the foundations mentioned in the Declaration, as "the overarching objectives of, and essential
requirements for sustainable development" bring to bear the intrinsic relevance of
both the Declaration and Plan of Implementation to air transport.

The Johannesburg Summit[35] also emphasized the concept of partnerships
between governments, while giving a large boost to business and civil society in
the Summit and the Plan of Implementation. Over 220 partnerships (with $235
million in resources) were identified in advance of the Summit and around 60
partnerships were announced during the Summit by a variety of countries. The
Summit also pledged its efforts towards Improving access to reliable, affordable,
economically viable, socially acceptable and environmentally sound energy services and resources, sufficient to achieve the Millennium Development Goal,[36]
including the goal of halving the proportion of people in poverty by 2015.

---

[33] See United Nations General Assembly Resolution 55/199.

[34] For the text of the Declaration see Johannesburg Declaration on Sustainable Development
(2002).

[35] See World Summit on Sustainable Development Plan of Implementation, (2002), http://www.
johannesburgsummit.org/html/documents/summit_docs/2309_planfinal.pdf.

[36] At its 5th Session in September 2000, the United Nations adopted Resolution A55/2—*United
Nations Millennium Declaration*—which recognizes that States have a collective responsibility to

A Workable Framework

The fundamental starting point for any discussion on sustainable development is the prospect of world population doubling in size at the end of the current century to 10 billion, at the rate of an increase of 95 million per yea (Serra 1996). Human population will remain the key indicator acting as a variable in determining the exploitative use of resources which will include a rapid consumption of non-renewable resources as well as the exhaustive use of renewable resources beyond the scope of their regenerative capacity. In this context, the failure of a society to generate a solution to the particular problem of consumption in excess of available resources would result in what is termed as "market failure". Market failure occurs when economic activity is undertaken without a full realization or study of its impact on the sustainability of the environment in which hat activity takes place.

The ICAO Assembly, at its 33rd Session held in September/October 2001, adopted Resolution (Consolidated Statement of Continuing ICAO Policies and Practices related to Environmental Protection) which recognizes the preamble to the Chicago Convention providing that the future development of international civil aviation can greatly help to create and preserve friendship and understanding among the nations and peoples of the world. Article 44 of the Chicago Convention states that ICAO should develop the principles and techniques of international air navigation and foster the planning and development of international air transport so as to meet the needs of the peoples of the world for safe, regular, efficient and economical air transport.

Resolution A33-7 also recognizes that many of the adverse environmental effects of civil aviation activity can be reduced by the application of integrated measures embracing technological improvements, appropriate operating procedures, proper organization of air traffic and the appropriate use of airport planning, land-use planning and management and market-based measures. In accordance with the Resolution, and in fulfilling its role, ICAO strives to achieve a balance between the benefit accruing to the world community through civil aviation and the harm caused to the environment in certain areas through the progressive advancement of civil aviation. ICAO is conscious of and will continue to take into account the adverse environmental impacts that may be related to civil aviation activity and its responsibility and that of its Contracting States to achieve maximum compatibility between the safe and orderly development of civil aviation and the quality of the environment.

(Footnote 36 continued)
uphold the principles of human dignity, equality and equity at the global level, notwithstanding their separate responsibilities. The Resolution reaffirmed States' commitment to the United Nations Charter and its relevance and capacity to inspire nations and peoples. The Resolution, inter alia called for shared responsibility for managing worldwide economic and social development.

In compliance with the objective of the Resolution, which is to ensure that regulation in aviation and environmental protection will maintain the essential balance between advancement of the aviation industry and sustainable development, the Council of ICAO will continue to pursue all civil aviation matters related to the environment and also maintain the initiative in developing policy guidance on these matters, and not leave such initiatives to other organizations. Also, in the spirit of A33-7, States have pledged to continue their active support for ICAO''s environment-related activities on all appropriate occasions.

The philosophical approach of Resolution A33-7 is a sound one in that the Resolution takes cognizance of the basic principle that environmental degradation is primarily caused by externalities which arise when a decision of some economic agent, such as a government or State instrumentality, affect other economic agents which are not factored into the overall equation of development. A classic example of environmental degradation in the field of aviation would be when a State takes a decision to adopt an open skies policy in order to attract tourism into its territory, resulting in a proliferation of air services into the country. Although in financial and economic terms such a measure would be profitable, the volume of environmental degradation in the country (particularly in the vicinity of the airports) would increase exponentially. There have been numerous analogies to this example, one being the case of Indonesia. The Indonesian Government taxed and later banned the import of timber, with a view to giving a boost to domestic sectors using timber as an element of production. This subsidy, although buttressing the local timber industry's economy, resulted in massive deforestation in the country as a result of local lumber enterprises trying to keep up with the evolving demand for timber products with the supply of local timber resource (See Primo Braga 1992). One must realize of course that trade per se is not a causative factor in environmental degradation but remains merely a contributory factor. It is in this sense that trade in air transport services, and in particular market access by air carriers, must be viewed as being potentially contributory to environmental degradation if trade aspects are not viewed by economic agents in conjunction with the environment.

The conceptual structure of Resolution A33-7 also lends itself well to recognizing that although economics and ecology has been mutually exclusive from a historical perspective, this perception has now changed, underscoring the current need to integrate the two, bringing together the complex and multi dimensional issues involved. Within the context of the air transport field, this merger has to be viewed on the basis that neither trade liberalization—which is the current trend in air transport market access—nor environmental protection is an end in itself, but remains a means towards achieving a harmonious blending of the elements of development and restraint contemporaneously so that sustainable development is ensured.

Resolution A33-7 also addressed growing concerns about environmental problems in the atmosphere such as global warming and depletion of the Ozone layer, noting that the Agenda 21 action plan adopted by the 1992 United Nations Conference on Environment and Development calls on governments to address these problems with the cooperation of relevant United Nations bodies. Particular mention is made to the Kyoto Protocol, adopted by the Conference of the Parties to the United Nations Framework Convention on Climate Change (UNFCC) in December 1997 (referred to in some detail later on) which recognizes ICAO as the primary body responsible for the regulation of aviation-related environmental issues on aircraft engine emission, and which calls upon developed countries to pursue limitation or reduction of greenhouse gases from "aviation bunker fuels" working through ICAO.

The Assembly recognized that market-based measures, which will be described in some detail later in this paper, are policy tools that are designed to achieve environmental goals at a lower cost and in a more flexible manner than traditional regulatory measures. Particularly in the context of controlling greenhouse gas emissions, the Assembly recognized that there has been increasing recognition by governments of the need for each economic sector to pay the full cost of the environmental damage it causes and market-based measures for protecting the environment were particularly relevant in this regard. It was the Assembly's view that any charges imposed, based on the costs of the mitigating or environmental impact of aircraft engine emissions to the extent that such costs can be properly identified and directly attributable to air transport, should be applicable only insofar as they are consistent with Article 15 of the Chicago Convention and ICAO's policies on taxes and charges.[37] The Assembly noted with approval analyses conducted by CAEP, that an open emissions trading system, whereby the total amount of emissions would be capped and allowances in the form of permits to emit carbon dioxide could be bought and sold to meet emission reduction objectives, was a cost effective measure to limit or reduce carbon dioxide emitted by civil aviation, particularly in the long term. Short term voluntary measures, where industry and governments agree to a target and/or to a set of actions to reduce emissions, would serve as a first step towards such long measures.

The Assembly required the Council of ICAO to develop guidance for States on the application of marketbased measures aimed at reducing or limiting the environmental impact of aircraft engine emissions, particularly with respect to mitigating the impact of aviation on climate changes. Above all, Contracting States and the Council are encouraged through Resolution A33-7 to take into account the interests of all parties concerned, to evaluate the costs and benefits of various measures with the goal of addressing aircraft engine emissions in the most cost effective manner and to adopt actions consistent with ICAO policies. The Assembly endorsed the development of an open emissions trading system for international aviation and requested the Council to develop guidelines for open emissions trading for international aviation, as a matter of priority.

---

[37] ICAO's policies on taxes and charges are contained in Doc 8632. These policies recommend, inter alia, the reciprocal exemption from all taxes levied on fuel taken on board by aircraft in connection with international air services, and reduction, to the fullest possible extent or elimination of taxes related to the sale or use of international air transport.

In making its recommendations and requests, the Assembly took into consideration the work of the CAEP which, at its Fifth Meeting (CAEP/5), held from 8 to 17 January 2001, CAEP identified market-based measures as being policy tools that are designed to achieve environmental goals at a lower cost and in a more flexible manner than traditional regulatory measures. CAEP considered three types of measures: emissions-related levies: generically, referring to charges and taxes; emissions trading: a system whereby the total amount of emissions would be capped and allowances in the form of permits could be bought and sold to meet emission reduction objectives; and voluntary measures: mechanisms under which industry and governments agree to a target and/or a set of actions to reduce emissions.

Under emission-related levies three options were considered by CAEP: a fuel (or en-route emissions) tax with revenue going to the national treasury; a revenue-neutral aircraft efficiency charge; and an en-route emissions charge with revenue returned to the aviation sector.

The main findings of the analysis conducted by CAEP on these three options are that, in the context of a fuel tax, it raises legal issues concerning air services agreements and ICAO policies, and, if not applied worldwide, could cause tankering practices (by which aircraft would carry extra fuel for later segments rather than purchasing the fuel locally). With regard to a revenue-neutral charge, CAEP felt that it would be consistent with ICAO policies but would require an acceptable method to be developed for defining aircraft efficiency, and could not be implemented in those areas which do not have en-route charges. An en-route emissions charge would be consistent with ICAO policies, assuming that revenues were recycled to the aviation sector, but, if not applied worldwide, could raise equity and competitiveness issues and would necessitate further guidance for the use and distribution of the revenue collected.

In designing an emission trading regime, It was the view of CAEP that the key issues are the scope of trading (that is open trading across sectors, or closed trading within the aviation sector alone), and the distribution of emission permits or allowances (i.e. grand-fathering, based on past or current use, or auctioning through a bidding process). Since such a system is untested for aviation, there would need to be rules for participation and the establishment of administrative mechanisms for recording trades and monitoring and ensuring compliance.

As for voluntary measures, CAEP advised the ICAO Council that an industry initiative, where a set of actions and/or a target to be met should be proposed, based on a negotiated agreement between industry and government to take a set of actions, and/or to achieve a specific emission target; and an hybrid option, under which one of the two above mentioned options is used in conjunction with another market-based measure.

The main findings were that voluntary measures alone cannot achieve an ambitious emission reduction target. They would have to be used in conjunction with other measures. In addition, these voluntary measures allow industry to enhance its ability to undertake activities related to "capability building". They are primarily looked at as transitional measures. A key issue is the need to ensure that any such action would be to the advantage of the participants if market based or other regulatory measures were imposed at a later date.

CAEP/5 concluded that a closed emissions trading system does not show cost benefit results to justify further consideration, and felt that an open emissions trading system would be a cost effective solution for CO_2 emission reductions in the long term, but cannot be implemented until the Kyoto protocol has entered into force and an emissions cap has been agreed. Further work is necessary to develop an emission trading system and to study the consequences for developing countries and ICAO should continue to play a leadership role, particularly in the development of proposals for caps, consistent with the responsibility given to ICAO in Article 2.2 of the Kyoto Protocol.

Emissions Trading as a Market Based Measure

The essential philosophy of emissions-trading in environmental protection is based on a certain flexibility allowed to market forces to reach the lowest cost involved in an operation whilst at the same time achieving an environmental target which has been already set. The word "trading" correctly denotes an exchange, and when applied to the aviation context means a certain trade-off between airlines whose fleets pollute more than others and low polluting airlines. The trade-off could take the form of a "purchase" by the high polluting airline of the reduction level of a low polluting airline. Emissions trading would encourage airlines to seek innovation in technology and to reduce their emission levels.

Emissions trading of levels of pollution between airlines differs fundamentally with the existing expectation of each airline maintaining a standard level of emission by its aircraft. When airlines would trade emission levels, the rates at which their aircraft pollute the atmosphere will be taken as a whole and applicable to a whole fleet, so that an airline which is over and above its permitted pollution level could join with another airline which is below the standard level of pollution required of it, thus making the average pollution between the two more acceptable than if taken individually. This mechanism encourages a low polluting airline to achieve even lower standards, in order to trade its levels with high polluting airlines.

The Third Conference of the Parties to the United Nations Framework Convention on Climate Change (Climate Change Convention)[38] was held from1 to 11 December 1997 at Kyoto, Japan. Significantly the States parties to the Convention adopted a protocol (Kyoto Protocol)[39] on 11 December 1997 under which

---

[38] (1992) 31 I.L.M.849. On the negotiations and text of the Climate Change Convention see Bodansky (1993). See also Barrett (1991).

[39] Kyoto Protocol to the United Nations Framework Convention on Climate change, UN Doc. FCCC/CP/1997/L.7/Add.1.

industrialized countries have agreed to reduce their collective emissions of six greenhouse gases[40] by at least 5 % by 2008–2012. Ambassador Raul Estrada-Oyuela, who had chaired the Committee of the Whole established by the Conference to facilitate the negotiation of a Protocol text, expressed the view that the agreement will have a real impact on the problem of greenhouse gas emissions and that 11 December 1997 should be remembered as the Day of the Atmosphere"[41]

The Kyoto Protocol, in Article 1 (a) (v) calls each State Party to achieve progressive or phasing out of market imperfections, fiscal incentives, tax and duty exemptions and subsidies in all greenhouse gas emitting sectors that run counter to the objective of the Convention and application of market instruments. The subject of emissions leading to trading is addressed initially in Article 3 of the Protocol which requires States Parties to ensure that their aggregate anthropogenic carbon dioxide equivalent emissions of the greenhouse gases listed in Annex A do not exceed their assigned amounts, calculated pursuant to their quantified emission limitation and reduction commitments inscribed in Annex B. The provision also requires States parties to the Protocol to reduce their overall emissions of greenhouse gases by at least 5 % below 1990 levels in the commitment period 2008–2012. Article 3 (6) goes further, in providing that States Parties shall be allowed a certain degree of flexibility in implementation of Article 3 and the reduction of their emission standards.

The subject of emissions-trading is explicitly addressed in Article 6 which states that for the purpose of meeting its commitments under Article 3, any Party included in Annex 1 may transfer to or acquire from, any other such Party emission reduction units resulting from projects aimed at reducing anthropogenic emissions by sources or enhancing anthropogenic removals by sinks of greenhouse gases in any sector of the economy provided the parties concerned approve of such trading; and, inter alia, such trading actually results in a reduction in emission by sources.

Article 17 sets out that the Conference of the Parties shall define the relevant principles, modalities, rules and guidelines, in particular for verification, reporting and accountability for emissions trading. It also provides that the parties included in Annex B to the Protocol may participate in emissions trading for the purposes of fulfilling their commitments under Article 3. Such trading shall be supplemental to domestic actions for the purpose of meeting qualified emission limitation and reduction commitments under Article 3.[42]

---

[40] Carbon dioxide, methane, nitrous oxide, hydro fluorocarbons, per fluorocarbons and sulphur hexafluoride.

[41] UN Environment Programme (UNEP) Press Release, 11 Dec 1997.

[42] The subject of emissions-trading falls within the purview of the Intergovernmental Panel on Climate Change (IPCC), which was established in 1988 by the World Meteorological Organization and the United Nations' Environment Programme (UNEP) to assess the scientific basis and impact of climate change. The IPCC's first scientific report was published in 1990 and recommended the negotiation of a framework convention to combat global warming. The United Nations Framework Convention on Climate Change (UNFCCC) was adopted on 9 May 1992 and

Once the Protocol has entered into force,[43] Annex I parties must submit an annual inventory of emissions to the Convention Secretariat,[44] enabling expert review teams to provide a full assessment of such parties' compliance with the Protocol.[45] These expert assessments will be reviewed by the Conference of the Parties serving as the meeting of the parties to the Protocol,[46] which will adopt decisions on implementation.[47]

Article 12 of the Protocol is also noteworthy in that it defines a clean development mechanism (CDM) which introduces the concept of joint implementation by a developed country and a developing country (See Parikh 1995). The mechanism admits of the advantage afforded to the parties concerned, in developed countries gaining the benefit of the partnerships in emissions-trading with developing countries which are more cost-effective in financing such projects. The CDM achieves the dual goal of enabling developing countries to operate projects which result in emission reductions which contribute to the objectives of the UNFCCC[48]—and also enabling countries specified in Annex I of the Kyoto Protocol which finance such projects through the CDM to use emissions reductions to reduce their own emissions in toto.[49]

The mechanism is supervised by an executive board and the responsibility of establishing procedures to make certain that proper verification of projects is achieved in a transparent manner devolve upon to the Conference of the Parties to the Protocol.[50] By virtue of Articles 12 (10) and 3 (12), Annex I countries could contribute to their own emission reduction targets under the Protocol by using emission reductions from jointly implemented projects under the CDM during the period 2000–2008.

(Footnote 42 continued)

the treaty entered into force on 21 March 1994. This article, being a legal one, will not address details of these bodies. For an extensive treatment of the IPCC's work and the UNFCC, see Global Warming and the Kyoto Protocol, Colin Warbrick and Dominic McGoldric ed., 47 *ICLQ*, April 1998 at pp. 446–462.

[43] The Protocol will enter into force 90 days after "not less than 55 Parties to the [Climate Change] Convention, incorporating Parties included in Annex 1 which accounted in total for at least 55 % of the total carbon dioxide emissions for 1990 of the Parties included in Annex 1" have ratified (Art. 24 of the Protocol).

[44] Id., Art. 7 (1). The Secretariat is located in Bonn, Germany. Its postal address is P.O. Box 260 124, D-53153, Bonn, Germany.

[45] Id., Art. 8 (1).

[46] Id., Art. 8 (5). When the Conference of the Parties meets as the meeting of Parties to the Protocol, those States that are party to the Convention but not to the Protocol may participate but only as non-voting observers (*idem*, Art. 13 (1) and (2)). Parties to the Protocol will meet annually (Art. 13 (6)) to review the implementation of the Protocol (Art. 13 (4)).

[47] Id., Art. 8 (6).

[48] *Supra*, see note 91.

[49] See Article 12 (3) of the Kyoto Protocol.

[50] Article 8 of the Protocol.

A watershed provision of the Kyoto Protocol lies in Article 2.2 which stipulates that Parties included in Annex II shall pursue limitation or reduction of emissions of greenhouse gases not controlled by the Montreal Protocol[51] from aviation and marine bunker fuels, working through the International Civil Aviation Organization and the International Maritime Organization respectively. This lays the regulatory responsibility for emissions-trading with regard to aircraft engine emissions squarely on ICAO.

Resolution A32-8 of ICAO, referred to earlier, and containing a consolidated statement of continuing ICAO policies and practices related to environmental protection urges States to refrain from unilateral environmental measures that would be harmful to the development of international civil aviation. On the subject of aircraft engine emissions, the Resolution, in its Appendix F, makes mention of the fact that the Kyoto Protocol calls for developed countries to pursue limitation or reduction of greenhouse gases from aviation bunker fuels, working through ICAO, and invokes Appendix A which calls upon the ICAO Council to maintain the initiative in developing policy guidance on all aviation matters related to the environment and not leave such initiatives to other organizations.

Appendix H of A32-8 refers to ICAO's policies on charges and taxes[52] and the policy statement issued by the ICAO Council on 9 December 1996 in the form of a Council Resolution of an interim nature, and urges States to follow the current guidance of the Council on emission-related levies. The Council is similarly exhorted by the Assembly, through A32-8, to continue to pursue the question of emission-related levies with a view to reaching a conclusion prior to the next ordinary Session of the Assembly in 2001.

The policy statement of the Council dated 9 December 1996 takes into consideration the fact that a number of States consider it desirable to use a levy to reflect environmental costs associated with air transport, while other States do not consider it appropriate to impose such a levy under the present circumstances. The Council goes on to state that it considers the development of an internationally-agreed environmental charge or tax on air transport that all States would be expected to impose would appear not to be practicable at the time, given the differing views of States and the significant organization and practical implementation problems that would be likely to arise.

According to the Council Statement, ICAO is seeking to identify a rational common basis on which States wishing to introduce environmental levies on air transport could do so. The Council strongly recommends in its Statement that any

---

[51] Montreal Protocol on Substances that Deplete the Ozone Layer (1987) 26 *I.L.M.* 1550. The Montreal Protocol controls gases such as chlorofluorocarbons, which not only have ozone depleting characteristics but also contribute to the greenhouse effect. The Kyoto Protocol has, by explicitly excluding the Montreal Protocol's role in ICAO's mandate, has included carbon dioxide, nitrogen oxides and compounds of sulphur emissions within ICAO's purview.

[52] As contained in Doc 9082 (*Statements by the Council to Contracting States on Charges for Airports and Air Navigation Services*) and Doc 8632 (*ICAO' Policies on Taxation in the Field of International Air Transport*).

environmental reviews on air transport which States may introduce should be in the form of charges rather than taxes and that the funds collected should be applied in the first instance to mitigating the environmental impact of aircraft engine emissions, for example by:

(a) addressing the specific damage caused by these emissions, if that can be identified;
(b) funding scientific research into their environmental impact; or
(c) funding research aimed at reducing their environmental impact, through developments in technology and new approaches to aircraft opera. It is incontrovertible that, in recent times, there has been confluence of global community awareness of the significance of the interrelationship between trade and environment. Unfortunately, although this fact has emerged in sectors such as energy and agriculture, it has not permeated the air transport industry sufficiently for a cohesive and composite philosophy to emerge in trade and environment. The award of market access, open skies exchanges and trade reciprocity stands isolated from environmental impact studies that may be necessary to maintain an overall balance. Even though some may argue that the contribution of aviation to environmental degradation is negligible, and that economic prospects for air transport are gloomy at best, there is no room for doubt that prudence would dictate the need for a multilateral approach to the integration of trade and the environment in a mutually supportive manner. Air transport needs a predictable multilateral trading system in order to ensure sustainable development for developed and developing countries alike.

The United Nations scientific and technical information system has as its objective the accumulation and improvement of reliable and comparable scientific and technical information about environmental issues and the development and application of means of collecting, storing, retrieving and processing such information that will make it readily available to decision makers and specialist.[53] Industry and transportation is one area within the purview of the United Nations Environment Programme (UNEP) which has a mandate to support the improvement of methodologies for analyzing the relationship between environment and development of procedures for incorporating environmental considerations into development policies, planning and administration.[54] Be that as it may, the exclusive mandate given to ICAO by the *Chicago Convention* of 1944 to regulate on aviation issues, coupled with exclusive and explicit recognition in the 1997 *Kyoto Protocol* to UNFCC, that ICAO will be the regulatory body in charge of aviation and environmental issues pertaining to climate change, imposes on ICAO a certain exclusive mandate within the United Nations umbrella to be responsible

---

[53] UNEP, 1988 *Annual Report of the Executive Director*, UN Doc UNEP/GC. 15/4 (1989) at p. 54.
[54] UNEP/GCSS. 1/7/add.1 (Nairobi, 1988) at p. 91.

for regulatory issues relating to aviation and the environment. It is in this context that one should examine the issue of air transport and environment having a common framework for sustainable development.

The infrastructure for a global framework for air transport resides with ICAO, in particular with the recognition given to ICAO by the Kyoto Protocol, even if only in the area of engine emissions. The Chicago Convention—being the fundamental statutory instrument which charters ICAO's mandate and purpose endorses ICAO's role in Article 44 of the Convention, devolving responsibility on the Organization to develop principles and techniques of air navigation and to foster the planning and development of international air transport so as to, inter alia, insure the safe and orderly growth of international civil aviation throughout the world; meet the needs of the peoples of the world for safe, regular, efficient and economical air transpor[55] and promote generally the development of all aspects of international civil aeronautics.[56]

Taking into consideration that trade in market access pertaining to air transport services is not within the umbrella of the World Trade Organization, the regulation of market access has to consistently endeavour to obviate unsustainable patterns of economic activity which may exacerbate problems of pollution and resource depletion. In this respect, ICAO has already initiated externalities such as incorporating emissions trading as a market based option (See Abeyratne 1999), although such initiatives including the introduction of sustainable processes of environmental taxation proceed at different levels of progress and speed in different countrie (Brack 1996).

ICAO has also taken sustained action over the past decade to adopt regulatory measures both in the area of engine emissions and noise. For example, in following up on revisions made by the Council in June 2001, the 33rd Session of the Assembly Resolution A33-7, urged Contracting States to adopt a balanced approach to noise management, taking full account of ICAO guidance, applicable legal obligations, existing agreements, current laws and established policies, all to be given due consideration when addressing noise problems at international airports. Contracting States are urged to adopt appropriate mechanisms in implementing this balanced approach, notably: in establishing a transparent process based on objective, measurable criteria for the assessment of the noise problem; in evaluating likely costs and benefits of various measures with a view to achieving maximum environmental benefit; and in providing for dissemination of the evaluation results that may be used in consultation with stakeholders and dispute resolutions.

As part of the balanced approach, Resolution A33-7 encourages States, inter alia, to conduct studies, support research and technology programmes aimed at reducing noise at source and to work closely with each other to ensure that their noise management programmes are harmonized taking into consideration the

---

[55] Id. Article 44 (d).

[56] Id. Article 44 (i).

particular economic exigencies of developing countries and also taking particular care so as not to derogate the non-discrimination principle enshrined in Article 15 of the Chicago Conventio.[57]

Resolution A33-7, in Appendix D, urges Contracting States not to introduce any phase-outs of subsonic jet aircraft which exceed noise levels contained in Volume 1 of Annex 16 to the Chicago Convention before giving consideration to a clear determination as to whether normal attrition of existing fleets of such aircraft will provide the necessary protection of noise climates around airports and whether necessary protection can be achieved by regulators preventing their operations from adding such aircraft to their fleets through either purchase, or lease/charter/interchange or alternatively by incentives to accelerate fleet modernization. Before phasing out subsonic aircraft that may exceed the above mentioned noise levels, the Resolution also calls upon Contracting States to give careful thought to whether alternatively effective noise management can be achieved by applying regulations preventing operations of such aircraft through restrictions limited to airports and runways, the use of which has been identified and declared by these States as generating noise problems and limited to time periods when greater noise disturbance is caused. Finally, Contracting States are called upon to consider implications of any restrictions for other States concerned, through consultation and reasonable notification of the application of restrictions.

One of the most significant achievements of Resolution A33-7 lies in the skilful balance achieved in offering a compromise to Contracting States which, despite the above mentioned criteria, decide to phase out aircraft which comply with noise certificates Standards in Volume 1, Chap. 2 of Annex 16 but which exceed the noise levels in Volume 1, Chap. 3 of Annex 16. This compromise recommends that such States frame any restrictions so that Chap. 2 compliant aircraft of an individual operator which are operating at present to their territories may be withdrawn from such operations gradually, over a period of not less than 7 years. The Resolution also requests Contracting States not to restrict before the end of the above period the operations of any aircraft less than 25 years after the date of issue of its first individual certificates of airworthiness, and, not to restrict before the end of the period the operations of any presently existing wide-body aircraft or of any fitted with engines that have a by-pass ratio higher than 2–1. Contracting States are required to inform ICAO, as well as the other States concerned, of all restrictions imposed.

Finally, on the subject of noise, the Resolution urges States not to introduce measures to phase out aircraft which comply, through original certification or re-certification, with the noise certification standards in Volume 1, Chaps. 3 or 4 of Annex 16 and, in particular, not to impose any operating restrictions on Chap. 3 compliant aircraft, except as part of the balanced approach to noise management

---

[57] Article 15, inter alia, generally requires that any charges that may be imposed or permitted to be imposed by a Contracting State for the use of airports and air navigation facilities by aircraft shall not be higher than those that are payable by national aircraft of the State imposing such charges.

developed by ICAO and in accordance with Appendices C and E to the Resolution which address issues pertaining to phase-out of subsonic aircraft and local noise related operations at airports.

Resolution A33-7 also addressed growing concerns about environmental problems in the atmosphere such as global warming and depletion of the Ozone layer, noting that the Agenda 21 action plan adopted by the 1992 United Nations Conference on Environment and Development calls on governments to address these problems with the cooperation of relevant United Nations bodies. Particular mention is made to the Kyoto Protocol which recognizes ICAO as the primary body responsible for the regulation of aviation related environmental issues on aircraft engine emission, and which calls upon developed countries to pursue limitation or reduction of greenhouse gases from "aviation bunker fuels" working through ICAO.

The Assembly recognized that market based measures, are policy tools that are designed to achieve environmental goals at a lower cost and in a more flexible manner than traditional regulatory measures. Particularly in the context of controlling greenhouse gas emissions, the Assembly recognized that there has been increasing recognition by governments of the need for each economic sector to pay the full cost of the environmental damage it causes and market based measures for protecting the environment were particularly relevant in this regard. It was the Assembly's view that any charges imposed, based on the costs of the mitigating or environmental impact of aircraft engine emissions to the extent that such costs can be properly identified and directly attributable to air transport, should be applicable only insofar as they are consistent with Article 15 of the Chicago Convention and ICAO's policies on taxes and charge.[58] The Assembly noted with approval analyses conducted by CAEP, that an open emissions trading system, whereby the total amount of emissions would be capped and allowances in the form of permits to emit carbon dioxide could be bought and sold to meet emission reduction objectives, was a cost effective measure to limit or reduce carbon dioxide emitted by civil aviation, particularly in the long term. Short term voluntary measures, where industry and governments agree to a target and/or to a set of actions to reduce emissions, would serve as a first step towards such long measures.

Although admittedly economic activity in air transport, particularly in the movement of aircraft between States territories, does not portend catastrophic environmental consequences on a short term basis, it is now opportune to address trade in air transport and its effect on global environmental welfare as a composite whole, rather than retain the status quo of a bifurcated group of interests. In this context it may be a useful exercise to commission a study to assess the two areas and their synergies.

---

[58] ICAO's policies on taxes and charges are contained in Doc 8632. These policies recommend, inter alia, the reciprocal exemption from all taxes levied on fuel taken on board by aircraft in connection with international air services, and reduction, to the fullest possible extent or elimination of taxes related to the sale or use of international air transport.

The most critical factor that adversely affects environmental protection is that the global political structure which is based on the primacy of States as sovereign entities has created conditions detrimental to sustainable development. The significance of the demographic structure of the world and its varied political interests underscore the inevitable emergence of a dichotomy between exponential increases in population; the needs thereof and the limited resource base available for development to meet such needs. Therefore sustainable development must, as a necessity, be addressed within the context of balancing population and natural resources (UNFPA/Norman Myers 1991). It is within these parameters that a study should make an assessment whether air transport, in its different trade dimensions, is a distinct threat to sustainable development.

ICAO's Current Role

ICAO is at the defining crossroads of its continuing path towards achieving its aims and objectives as set out in the Convention on International Civil Aviation. With a view to setting its course in line with rapidly evolving trends of globalization and regionalization, the Organization has embarked on implementing an aggressive business plan that calls for a cultural transition and change of mind-set that rids ICAO from the shackles of the Convention. New leadership and new thinking have been catalysts in this process, and, through a fog of rhetoric which sometimes accused the Organization of being a bureaucracy that was rapidly headed towards obsolescence, a flight path seems to have cleared that enables the Organization to steer towards a more relevant role in the new century. This article traces this new role and suggests a way forward.

It is curious that, six decades after the establishment of the International Civil Aviation Organization (ICAO),[59] some still refer to its powers and functions (MacKenzie 2008). There are some others who allude to ICAO's mandate. The fact is that ICAO has only aims and objectives, recognized by the Convention on International Civil Aviation which established the Organization.[60] Broadly, those aims and objectives are to develop the principles and techniques of international air navigation and to foster the planning and development of international air transport. In effect, this bifurcation implicitly reflects the agreement of the

---

[59] ICAO is the specialized agency of the United Nations handling issues of international civil aviation. ICAO was established by the Convention on International Civil Aviation, signed at Chicago on 7 December 1944 (Chicago Convention). The overarching objectives of ICAO, as contained in Article 44 of the Convention is to develop the principles and techniques of international air navigation and to foster the planning and development of international air transport so as to meet the needs of the peoples for safe, regular, efficient and economical air transport. ICAO has 190 member States, who become members of ICAO by ratifying or otherwise issuing notice of adherence to the Chicago Convention.

[60] *Id.* Article 43.

international community of States which signed the Chicago Convention that
ICAO could adopt Standards in the technical fields of air navigation and could
only offer guidelines in the economic field. This exclusive right in the technical
field initially bestowed on ICAO the authority to set standards for equipment and
procedures on international air routes in the first years (1947–1949) of ICAO.[61]
This key task of standardizing technical specifications in air navigation gave rise to
the realization that, apart from States that were most advanced in technology and
could implement ICAO's standards, there were numerous other States who could
not implement the Standards, however, willing they would be, due to the lack of
resources and know-how.[62] This gave rise to offers of help by numerous member
States of ICAO, and the technical assistance limb of ICAO was born.

One has, however, to note that the position of ICAO as an incipient regulator
was quite different from the one it is placed in now. In 1949 ICAO was feeling the
pulse of the world of civil aviation and formulating regulations. This was the year
in which ICAO embarked upon a comprehensive study of the ground facilities
operated by governments and the services that they provided.[63] Traffic volumes
were only beginning to pick up and passengers and cargo between North America
and Europe were being carried by eleven carriers. Elsewhere, in South America
direct east-west services went into operation for the first time.[64]

Much water has flown under the bridge since then and ICAO now stands in a
world of civil aviation bewildered by its own progress and exponential demand for
capacity and services. ICAO's Annual Report of the Council for 2007 records that
the world economy maintained its growth momentum in 2007, despite higher
prices for crude oil and refined products, as the world gross domestic product
(GDP) grew at an estimated average annual rate of 4.9 % in real terms (Industrialized countries experienced a slight downturn compared to 2006, posting a
GDP growth rate of 2.6 %. Growth in emerging markets and developing countries
remained very strong at 7.8 %, well above the world average yet with significant
regional differences. The world trade volume in goods and services is estimated to
have grown by approximately 6.6 %. International tourist arrivals were up by an
estimated 5.7 %. According to the United Nations World Tourism Organization
(UNWTO), more than 880 million tourists travelled to foreign countries, some 32
million more than the previous year. The highest growth in arrivals was in the Asia
and Pacific Region at about 10.2 %, followed by Africa (8.8 %), the Middle East
(8.4 %), Europe (4.2 %) and the Americas (4.1 %).[65]

---

[61] Max Hymans, President of the Second ICAO Assembly observed in 1948 that the
standardization of equipment and procedures had progressed well and that ICAO had an
incontestable authority in this respect. See Hymens (1948).

[62] See ICAO Doc 6968, A4-P/1 Report of the Council to the Assembly on the Activities of the
Organization in 1949, 23 March 1950.

[63] Id. A4-P/1 23/3/50 at 1.

[64] Id. 2.

[65] *ICAO Annual Report of the Council—2007 A-1.*

The same report states that the liberalization of international air transport regulation continued to evolve at various levels.[66] It is estimated that this involved about 30 % of country-pairs with non-stop passenger air services and almost half of the frequencies offered, through either bilateral "open skies" air services agreements or regional liberalized agreements and arrangements. At the bilateral level, 9 new "open skies" agreements were concluded by 12 States, bringing the total to 136 agreements involving 91 States. These agreements provide for full-market access without restrictions on designations, route rights, capacity, frequencies, code-sharing and tariffs. At the regional level, at least 12 liberalized agreements or arrangements were in operation with the following noteworthy developments.

Intra regional cooperation towards liberalization has grown in recent times and was seen at its highest in 2007.[67] The EU was the most active, where the European Commission carried out specific negotiating mandates on behalf of all EU Member States. In April, the Air Transport Agreement was formally signed by the EU and the United States as a first stage for the creation of an Open Aviation Area. With provisional application from March 2008, the agreement replaces all existing bilateral air services agreements between the EU Member States and the United States. In October, the European Commission was given a new mandate to open negotiations with Canada on a comprehensive aviation agreement. At the multi-lateral level, the World Trade Organization (WTO) pursued the second review of the Annex to the General Agreement on Trade in Services (GATS) on Air Transport Services. Discussions focused on significant economic and regulatory developments in the air transport sector, such as low-cost carrier services and scheduled passenger and air cargo services. Talks also covered a proposal to extend the Annex to include ground-handling and airport operation services, in addition to the current three activities covered—aircraft repair and maintenance,

---

[66] In January 2007, the Single Aviation Market of the European Union (EU) was expanded from 25 to 27 States with the addition of Bulgaria and Romania; in February, the Association of South-East Asian Nations (ASEAN) further liberalized the Memorandum of Understanding on Air Freight Services originally signed in 2002. Also in February, the Agreement on the Liberalization of Air Transport between the Arab States came into force, initially for five Arab League States; and in October, the Pacific Islands Air Services Agreement came into force, initially for six Member States of the Pacific Islands Forum.

[67] Air transport liberalization also continued to develop at the national level as well. In November 2007, the Government of Japan liberalized access of foreign airlines to 23 regional airports in order to strengthen the country's position as a gateway for international traffic. In the same month, Pakistan adopted a new national aviation policy to further liberalize the air transport sector, including an "open skies" policy for cargo operations. The increase in mergers and the steady expansion of alliances, involving especially the three global groupings (Star Alliance, Oneworld, and SkyTeam), continued to attract attention from regulatory authorities. In February, the United States Department of Transportation (DOT) approved the application for antitrust immunity for an alliance agreement among nine airlines of Star Alliance. In October, the European Commission published commitments submitted by eight airlines of SkyTeam, a condition for obtaining approval for their alliance.

selling and marketing of air transport, and computer reservation system (CRS) services.

At the time of writing, preliminary estimates for 2007 indicated that the world's scheduled airlines as a whole experienced material operating profits and overall net profitability despite rising fuel prices.[68] Operating revenues of scheduled airlines of ICAO Contracting States were estimated at $484.7 billion and operating expenses for the same airlines at $468.4 billion, for an operating profit of 3.4 % of operating revenues.[69] This follows an operating profit of 2.9 % in 2006. Per tonne-kilometre, operating revenues increased from 83.3 cents in 2006 to an estimated 84.7 cents, while operating expenses increased from 51.3 cents to an estimated 52.1 cents.

This exponential growth in air traffic brings to bear the existence of a complex global civil aviation regulatory system that has transcended the stage of formulation and standardization and reached a stage of implementation of technical and commercial measures. This implementation is built upon the steady evolutionary flow of Standards, Recommended Practices and Guidelines of ICAO that have taken place over the past few decades. In the process, ICAO has evolved from being a bureaucratic machine that spewed regulation, to becoming a lean outfit of experts who are required to ensure that States implement, or be assisted in implementing what has been established as Standards and Recommended Practices in the Annexes to the Chicago Convention.

References

Abeyratne RIR (1999) Emissions trading as a market-based option in air transport—contractual issues. Environ Policy law 29(5):226–235

Atapattu SA (2006) Emerging principles of international environmental law. In: Series on international law and development. Transnational Publishers, Ardsley, p 1

Barrett J (1991) The negotiation and drafting of the climate change convention. In: Churchill R, Freestone D (eds) International law and global climate change. Martinus Nijhoff, Leiden, pp 183–200

Bodansky D (1993) The United Nations framework convention on climate change: a commentary. Yale J Int L 18:451–558

---

[68] The total scheduled traffic carried by the airlines of the 190 Contracting States of ICAO amounted to approximately 2,250 million passengers and some 41 million t of freight. The overall passenger/freight/mail tonne-kilometres performed increased some 5.5 % over 2006, with international tonne-kilometres at about 5.8 %. The growth in passenger traffic generally outpaced seat capacity offered. As a result, the average passenger load factor on total scheduled services (domestic and international) went up to 77 %, compared to 76 % in 2006. See *ICAO Annual Report of the Council—2007, supra* note 123, A-3.

[69] Strong growth rates across all regions for international passenger traffic continued in 2007, although globally at a marginally lower rate of 7.3 % compared to 7.6 % in 2006. The breakdown in terms of percentage of total traffic carried and of growth rates for carriers is as follows: Europe, 40 and 6.4; Asia/Pacific, 28 and 6.6; North America, 17 and 5.5; Middle East, 8 and almost 19; Latin America and Africa, 7, and 5.8 (Latin America) and 6.8 (Africa).

Brack D (1996) International trade and the Montreal protocol, The Royal Institute of International Affairs. Earthscan Publications Ltd, London, p 2

Christol CQ (1991) Space law past, present and future. Kluwer Law and Taxation Publishers, Deventer, p 231

Hymens M (1948) Results of a meeting. Interavia 3(8):422

Johannesburg Declaration on Sustainable Development (2002) A/CONF.199/l.6, http://www.johannesburgsummit.org/html/documents/summit_docs/1009wssd_pol_declaration.doc

MacKenzie D (2008) ICAO, a history of the international civil aviation organization. University of Toronto Press, Toronto, p 1

Mortimer LF (1992) Ambitious programme of future work to be undertaken by CAEP. ICAO J 47:6

Parikh JK (1995) Joint implementation and North South cooperation for climate change. Int Environ Aff 7(1):22–41

Primo Braga CA (1992) Tropical forests and trade policy: the case of Indonesia and Brazil. In: Low P (ed) International trade and the environment, Discussion Paper No. 159. World Bank, Washington D.C., pp 173–194

Serra R (1996) The causes of environmental degradation. In: Swanson TM (ed) The economics of environmental degradation. UNEP, Edward Elgar, Cheltenham, pp 82, 87

UNFPA/Norman Myers (1991) Population, resources and the environment: the critical challenges. UN Population Fund, New York, p 5

Chapter 3
Market Based Measures

Work Up to 2012

Seven years ago, The Fourth Assessment report produced by the Inter-Governmental Panel on Climate Change (IPCC)[1] released in 2007 bore strong evidence of continuing global warming:

> Warming of the climate is unequivocal, as is now evident from observations of increases in global average air and ocean temperatures, widespread melting of snow and ice, and rising average sea level.[2]

The Report further stated that observational evidence from all continents and many natural systems are being affected by regional climate change, particularly

---

[1] The IPCC is a scientific intergovernmental body set up by the World Meteorological Organization (WMO) and by the United Nations Environment Programme (UNEP). The IPCC was established to provide the decision-makers and others interested in climate change with an objective source of information about climate change. The IPCC does not conduct any research nor does it monitor climate related data or parameters. Its role is to assess on a comprehensive, objective, open and transparent basis the latest scientific, technical and socio-economic literature produced worldwide relevant to the understanding of the risk of human-induced climate change, its observed and projected impacts and options for adaptation and mitigation. IPCC reports should be neutral with respect to policy, although they need to deal objectively with policy relevant scientific, technical and socio economic factors. They should be of high scientific and technical standards, and aim to reflect a range of views, expertise and wide geographical coverage.

[2] *Climate Change 2007: Synthesis Report, an Assessment of the Inter-Governmental Panel on Climate Change* topic 1 at 30.

© The Author(s) 2014
R. Abeyratne, *Aviation and Climate Change*, SpringerBriefs in Law,
DOI: 10.1007/978-3-319-08443-5_3

through temperature increases.[3] The results of this increase in temperature through global warming include but are not limited to enlargement and increased numbers of glacial lakes; increasing ground instability in permafrost regions and rock avalanches in mountainous regions; and changes in some Arctic and Antarctic ecosystems.

One of the more ominous statements of the Report was that continued emissions from greenhouse gases[4] at or above current rates would cause further warming and induce many changes in the global climate system during the 21st century that would very likely be larger than those observed during the 20th century.

Warmer surface temperatures and warmer oceans give rise to increased evaporating water, resulting in increases in moisture in the atmosphere. Experts have attributed these increases in moisture and humidity in the recent past to the frequency and intensity of hurricanes and cyclones which occurred in the recent past, particular in reference to the strength and duration of the storms.

One commentator has said:

> If in the year 2030, carbon dioxide concentrations in the atmosphere remain as high as they are today, the likely result is two degrees centigrade warming (above pre industrial levels). Two degrees is the point beyond which certain ecosystems begin collapsing. Having, until then, absorbed carbon dioxide, they begin collapsing. Beyond this point, in other words climate change is out of our hands (Monbiot 2006).

How does aviation fit into this picture? Anita Rodick is sanguine but also very logical when she addresses the effects of growing tourism and travel by air in the coming decades and the result aircraft engine emissions may have on climate change:

> Some people are suspicious of the whole idea of ethical tourism, arguing that, to reach most places, you have to travel by air—which itself is unethical. It is true that government expects air travel passengers to double by 2030, by which time air travel will be the biggest contributor to global warming. However, it is also true that the airline industry can now create fuel efficiency planes.[5]

Indeed there has been some encouraging news on this front. In 2006 Virgin Atlantic Chairman, Sir Richard Branson formed a new company—Virgin Fuels—

---

[3] Id. 31. The IPCC also states that global atmospheric concentrations of CO_2, CH_4 and N_2O have increased markedly as a result of human activities since 1750 and now far exceed pre-industrial values determined from ice cores spanning many thousands of years. The atmospheric concentrations of CO_2 and CH_4 in 2005 exceed by far the natural range over the last 650,000 years. Global increases in CO_2 concentrations are due primarily to fossil fuel use, with land-use change providing another significant but smaller contribution. The Report further states that it is very likely that the observed increase in CH_4 concentration is predominantly due to agriculture and fossil fuel use. The increase in N_2O concentration is primarily due to agriculture. Id. Topic 2 at 37.

[4] Carbon dioxide, methane, nitrous oxide, hydro fluorocarbons, per fluorocarbons and sulphur hexafluoride.

[5] Anita Rodick, Travel That Doesn't Cost the Earth, *Independent*, 20 September 2005.

that would invest millions of dollars in alternate fuels.[6] He pledged to reinvest profits from his airline and rail transport businesses to alternative energy, explaining that his initiative was prompted by the concern he had regarding the welfare of the world affected by global warming.[7] This move is but part of Branson's actions to coerce the aviation industry to cut fuel consumption, for which he has set aside an investment of US$3 billion over the next 10 years to fight global warming.[8]

Branson's initiative, which is both laudable and timely, followed a secular trend where, since the time of the introduction of jet aircraft, civil aviation authorities had made inroads into the realm of fuel consumption and made sustained efforts to address the issue of environmental impacts caused by aircraft operations.[9] This was primarily because of the inevitable corollary to the exclusive use of petroleum as industrial fuel. This in turn resulted in the depletion of global oil reserves, where, as far back as 1949 (Hubbert 1949) oil was recognized as a finite non renewable resource. Both factors—pollution caused by engine emissions as well as the limits of global oil resources—prompted wide ranging studies on the optimal use of fuel in the aviation industry and alternative fuel sources.[10]

Being already aware of this trend, Ryanair, known to be Europe's greenest airline, invested some E17 billion on its fleet replacement and expansion programme which began in 1999. All of Ryanair's older Boeing 737-200 aircraft have already been replaced with next generation 737-800 aircraft, which has made Ryanair the airline with the youngest and most modern fleet in all of Europe. These measures put Ryanair in the forefront as an airline which minimises and continues to reduce fuel burn and carbon dioxide emissions per passenger kilometre. The low cost business model used by Rayanair (and other low cost carriers) which involves the use of secondary airports with no holding patterns as in busier airports and point to point services (which eliminate multiple landings) help increase fuel efficiency and restrict emissions. It is reported that Ryanair's fleet replacement has

---

[6] Virgin's Branson Tackles Emissions, Forms Fuel Company, *Aviation Daily*, Thursday, September 28, 2006 at 1.

[7] Virgin Territory, Richard Branson's Move to cut Greenhouse Gas Emissions, *The Economist*, September 30th 2006, 65. This concern is apparently justified as carbon emissions from airlines rose approximately by 12 % in 2004, as reported by the environmental campaign group, *Friends of the Earth. Ibid.*

[8] *Aviation Daily, supra*, note 6, at 1.

[9] Aircraft fuel efficiency has improved by some 50 % over the past 30 years through advances in engine and airframe technology. See *IATA/ATAG Aviation and Environment Brochure*, (1997) at 7.

[10] It must be noted that steady progress has since been made. Aircraft entering today's fleets are 70 % more fuel efficient than they were four decades ago. Carbon Monoxide emissions have been simultaneously reduced by unburned hydrocarbons and smoke has been cut by 90 %. see http://www.atag.org/content/showfacts.asp?folderid=430&levell=2&level2=430&.

resulted in an overall reduction in fuel consumption of 52 % between 1998 and 2006.[11]

On the other side of the Atlantic, American Airlines, with one of the largest fleets in the world, was also involved in a comprehensive aircraft weight-reduction program. The airline removed ovens and galleys from aircraft on which hot food is not served. It also carried less potable water on flights. Although earlier it was routine for maintenance personnel to simply fill the water tanks prior to flight, a study conducted by the airline revealed that usually less than half the water was being consumed. Following this realization, the maintenance department designed a $1 valve that shuts off the filler hose when the tank reaches 75 % capacity rather than change the water-tank filling procedure, which resulted in a reduction of aircraft weight by about 100 pounds and a saving of approximately $2.8 million in fuel annually.

Another proactive measure adopted by American was to set up an engine wash program to remove debris and carbon deposits from power plants, which allows them to run more efficiently and burn less fuel. This program saved about 4 million gallons of fuel per year. The carrier has found ways to burn less kerosene on the ground. Instead of running the auxiliary power unit (APU) while an aircraft is in for maintenance, technicians plug the airplane into ground power or pre-conditioned air units. Furthermore, American is beginning to use high-speed tractor tugs to move airplanes into the maintenance hangar so that engines are not used to taxi the aircraft.

Alaska Airlines is another American carrier which took measures to conserve fuel by reducing burn. It adopted many of the same fuel-savings measures that American and other carriers have implemented. An audit conducted by Alaska revealed that the airline was doing everything that manufacturers recommended in terms of maintenance. However, the audit report recommended performing engine washes with hot water instead of cold to make them more effective. Alaska also considered certain fuel- and weight-saving product improvements. The carrier plans to have CFM 56 engine-performance improvement kits installed on its 737s, and the airline considered putting carbon brakes on those planes, a measure that would save almost 800 pounds.

It is widely accepted by experts that the key to maximizing fuel efficiency is minimizing increases in aircraft drag, especially those associated with control surfaces that are out of rig and aerodynamic seals that are leaking. They also recommend that operators look closely at gaps between fairings and external panels.[12] Bad door seals impose a double penalty because the air conditioning system has to work harder, and leaking air can disrupt airflow around the airplane and increase drag.[13]

---

[11] This compares well with British Airways figure of 27 % improvement in fuel efficiency between 1990 and 2005. See http://www.ryanair.com/site/EN/about.php?page=About&sec=environment. Also, *British Airways Annual Report* 2006.

[12] Robert A Searles, Maintaining for Fuel Efficiency, *Overhaul and Maintenance*, October 2006, at 32.

[13] Ibid.

In the final analysis, however, only a small part of fuel inefficiency can be attributed to the airframe. Most is caused by the way the engines are operated. For example, use of higher takeoff thrust can cause the fuel mileage of engines to deteriorate more rapidly. Conversely, using reduced takeoff thrust can save fuel. Recent studies have revealed that efforts at reducing engine noise contemporaneously result in reduction of fuel burn. A significant innovation in this regard is the continuous descent approach (CDA) which veers from the traditional "staircase" approach of landing, where the aircraft begins descending many miles from the runway, spending substantial time at low altitudes. Planes descend usually in "steps" incurring substantial fuel burn and noisy engine thrusts. The CDA keeps aircraft at cruise altitude until they are in close proximity to an airport when they can make an even, continuous landing approach. The CDA, which was a research project of the Massachusetts Institute of Technology (MIT),[14] drastically reduces the noise of an aircraft at approach and landing, and significantly reduces fuel consumption experienced with the "staircase" approach.

In another combined Cambridge University/MIT effort engineers came up with what they believed was the future for commercial airliners—a radical "flying wing" designed to be so quiet that no one outside an airport will be able to hear it. Called the SAX-40, the flying wing would be 25 % more fuel-efficient than modern planes and carry 215 passengers up to 5,000 nautical miles (5,750 miles) at a maximum speed of 600 mph.[15] The engineers involved in the project have calculated that the SAX-40 would achieve 149 passenger miles per gallon compared with 121 for a Boeing 777. By comparison a Toyota Prius hybrid car gets 144 passenger miles per gallon. This blended wing design concept, which could come into commercial service by 2030,[16] is a result of the £2.3 m Silent Aircraft Initiative (SAI), a 3-year collaboration between Cambridge University and the Massachusetts Institute of Technology.

The most disturbing fact regarding achieving lower fuel consumption is that, unlike other transportation sectors, aviation currently has no viable alternative to burning fossil fuels, although encouraging steps have been taken in the field of alternative furels and, at the time of writing a few airlines were using a mix of fossil-bio fuels on some of their flights. It is reported that aviation currently consumes 2–3 % of all fuels burnt. Whereas the entire transportation sector

---

[14] Quieter, Cleaner airplane Landings on the Way, *MIT News* January 13 2005 at http://web.mit.edu/newsoffice/2005/noise.html.

[15] AlokJha, On a Wing and a Whisper: The airliner to End Runway Noise, *The Guardian*, Tuesday November 7 2006 at 4.

[16] It must be borne in mind that this is a conceptual design and there are many technological barriers that need to be overcome to introduce these technologies into commercial use. Experts at Cambridge University have outlined challenges such as developing the strong composite materials needed to produce the oval-shaped hull and improving modern jet engines to work with the SAX-40 design. However, these challenges can be overcome and work is progressing within the Silent Aircraft Initiative.

consumes 20–25 % of all fuel consumed by industry and domestic home environments. Of this, road transportation uses 75 % while aviation consumes 12 %.[17]

The importance of reducing fuel burn by aircraft engines and the looming threat for the aviation community of having to look for alternative means of fuelling aircraft cannot be appreciated fully without an extrapolation of the significance of aviation to world commerce and tourism. The Air Transport Action Group (ATAG) of IATA reported that aviation transports globally 2 billion passengers every year and 40 % of the inter-regional goods by value. 40 % of tourists now travel by air and the air transport industry generates a total of 29 million jobs annually through direct, indirect and catalytic impacts.[18] Aviation's global economic impact is valued at US$2.960 billion which is equivalent to 8 % of the world's gross domestic product.[19]

In addition to its total output and employment impacts, civil aviation has a broader influence on overall economic growth, deriving from non-quantifiable benefits for the users of air transport, businesses and individuals alike. Air transport acts as a facilitator for the development of markets and trading of goods as well as services. In 2005, airline scheduled services carried 2.022 billion passengers (at an annual increase of 7.1 % over 2004) and 37.7 million tonnes of freight worldwide (at an annual increase of 2.5 %).[20] Approximately 45 % of some 714 million international tourists and some 40 % by value of the world's manufactured exports were transported by air that year.

Measuring the economic contribution of civil aviation helps one understand that air transport, aerospace and other affected industries have a significant impact in generating output and creating employment throughout a given economy. For the provision of air travel and freight services, air carriers and other operators purchase a wide range of products (goods and services) mainly from airports, air navigation services providers, governmental agencies, public corporations as well as aerospace manufacturing and other industries.

At the national level, the stimulating economic impact of civil aviation as job creator and contributor to economic growth is evident when airlines, airports, air navigation services providers and aerospace industries and their respective affiliates meet a growing direct demand for air transport services by expanding operations and fleets, ordering more goods and services from suppliers, hiring more employees and thus increasing their outputs. These direct economic activities have multiplier effects upon other industries throughout an economy. A wider or narrower spread of

---

[17] Air Travel, Greener by Design, the Challenge, see http://www.foresight.gov.uk/Previous_Rounds/Foresight_1999__2002/Defence_Aerospace_and_Systems/Reports/Air%20Travel%20Challenge/The_Challenge.pdf.

[18] http://www.atag.org/content/showfacts.asp?folderid=430&levell=2&level2=430&.

[19] Ibid.

[20] *Annual Report of the Council*, 2005 Appendix 13 p. A-98.

these multipliers will depend on the circumstances, notably the size of the industries associated with civil aviation and the assessment approach taken. For example, States with significant aerospace manufacturing industries will show a wide spread, while those with limited air transport services may have a relatively narrow spread. Non-aviation travel and tourism businesses, such as hotels and restaurants, travel agencies, tour operators and retailers greatly benefit from trip-related expenses of airline passengers.

The United States has shown exponential growth in the aviation industry and as such the impetus of civil aviation in the United States economy a good case study to demonstrate the impact of the economic contribution of civil aviation. It has been evaluated over a number of years by Wilbur Smith Associates on behalf of the U.S. Federal Aviation Administration. In 2000 (the most recent year for which data are available), the provision of airline services, general aviation activities, airport operations and acquisition of aircraft totalled an output value of US$177.3 billion and created more than 1.2 million jobs. Expenditures associated with business and leisure trips by air totalled US$176.3 billion and created over 3.1 million jobs. These direct and catalytic expenditures generated additional expenditures of US$654.6 billion and over 5.5 million jobs through the indirect demand of suppliers and induced demand effects.

These results for the U.S. economy can also be expressed as "multiplier effects" of the direct demand: every US$100 of output produced and every 100 jobs created by civil aviation in 2000 trigger another US$469 of output and 717 jobs in many different industries. The value of all economic activities of civil aviation and air travel-related expenses, plus indirect and induced multiplier effects, totalled US$1008.2 billion and employed 10 million people who earned US$310.1 billion in 2000. Compared to 1987, total output increased by 27.4 %, while the number of jobs increased by 23.7 % and income rose by 31.8 %.[21]

Elsewhere in another busy air transport market—in the United Kingdom, aviation grew faster than any other source of greenhouse gases between 1990 and 2004. During this time, the number of persons using airports grew by 120 % and the energy consumed by aircraft serving the United Kingdom grew by 79 % the CO_2 emissions are reported to have risen by almost 100 % (5.5 % of all CO_2 emissions produced by the country).[22] The British Government had also predicted that if things were to run as usual (i.e. if air transport growth was to occur untrammelled), the 200 million passengers handled in British airports in 2003 would increase up to between 400 and 600 million passengers in 2030.[23] Again, this is "predict and provide" philosophy which if let to go unchecked, would end up in catastrophe.

---

[21] Id., at 12.

[22] Monbiot, See References at the end of the chapter, at 174.

[23] Department of Transport, White Paper: The Future of Air Transport December 2003 at p/23.

It must be noted that the IPCC special report on *Aviation and the Global Atmosphere*[24] developed in response to a request from ICAO, addressed sector specific impact of aviation on climate change based on evaluation of consequences of greenhouse gases from aircraft engines and the potential effects from aviation on stratospheric ozone depletion and global climate change. The Report came to the conclusion that the contribution made by aviation to the total radiative forcing (which, in other words is a measure of change in climate) from all human activities was 3.5 % and that this percentage which did not take into consideration the effects of possible changes in cirrus clouds was expected to grow.[25]

On a general basis, and in terms of overall transportation and its effect on climate change, the ICAO Committee on Aviation Environmental Protection (CAEP), at its eighth meeting held in Montreal from 1–12 February 2010, acknowledged that while aviation accounted for 11.5 % of CO_2 emissions, maritime transport was responsible for emitting 9.7 % while rail took fourth place with 1.9 %. The largest contributor was road transportation with 77 %.[26]

ICAO's forecast, called the *Climate Change Outlook* also released in 2010 reflects that total aviation CO_2 emissions (domestic and international) are approximately 2 % of the world's anthropogenic (human made) CO_2 emissions. The Report goes on to say that international flights are responsible for approximately 62 % of these emissions and that the amount of CO_2 emissions from aviation is projected to grow around 3–4 % per annum. ICAO's conclusion is that medium term mitigation for CO_2 emissions from the aviation sector can potentially come from improved fuel efficiency, although such efficiency improvements are only expected to partially offset the continuing increase in aviation CO_2 emissions.[27]

Although the effects of climate change are not so prominent in the human sphere as in the natural world, there is palpable evidence that problems related to the supply of water will increasingly appear as a result of shrinking glaziers, drought, snow pack, evaporation and the infiltration of salt water in areas below sea level. The IPCC Assessment Report suggests mitigation measures such as demand side management brought to bear through behavioural changes that promote conservation of energy; introduction of technologies that improve energy efficiency; and carbon capture and storage.[28] The potential costs involved in affecting such mitigation is set at 1 % of the global GDP.

---

[24] *Aviation and the Global Atmosphere*, Intergovernmental Panel on Climate Change (WMO, UNEP), A Special Report of IPCC Working Groups 1 and II, Cambridge University Press: Cambridge, 1999.

[25] Id. at 21.

[26] *Report of the Committee on Aviation Environmental Protection*, Eighth Meting, Montreal, 1–12 February 2010, ICAO Doc 9938, CAEP/8 at 1–38.

[27] Climate Change Outlook—ICAO Environmental Report 2010, Montreal: 2010 at 31.

[28] *Climate Change 2007...*, *supra*, note 2 at 37.

Action Taken

In 2012, ICAO undertook a study calculated to result in a framework of market based measures that would respond globally to the adverse effects of aircraft engine emissions. This was in direct response to a call by 26 member States of the ICAO Council including China, Russia, India and the United States which, in late 2011 had protested against the emissions trading scheme (EU ETS) of the European Union applicable to air transport. As a result the Council adopted a Declaration supporting the position of the protesting States[29] which opposed the unilateral application of the EU ETS on international aviation and urged continued collaborative action on a global sectoral approach to aviation greenhouse gas emissions that was provisionally agreed by the 190 ICAO Member States of ICAO in 2010. At the time of writing, the United States Senate and the Obama administration had further strengthened their opposition to the EU ETS and, in a rare exhibition of bipartisanship the Republican members of the Commerce Committee had also joined in. In an official statement, Transportation Secretary Ray LaHood had acknowledged ICAO as the appropriate body to establish a global framework that would govern market based measures relating to aircraft engine emissions.[30] As an active measure aimed at supporting the thrust of US opposition, it has been suggested that the issue might be brought for consideration before the Council under Article 84 of the Chicago Convention.[31] I will not go into a deep discussion on this issue as I have written extensively about it in my earlier publications (See Abeyratne 2011, 2012a, b). My interest, in this book, is to offer an approach that ICAO could take without fragmenting the issue of engine emissions from the systemic

---

[29] The Declaration called on the EU and its member states to exclude non-EU carriers from the EU ETS was endorsed by the ICAO Council in November 2011. All 26 states are members of the 36-strong Council, leaving eight EU states to oppose the adoption and two abstentions—Australia and Canada. It was made clear during the meeting that the adoption of the Declaration had no legally binding effect on any member state or the Council but it will serve as another political reminder of the strong opposition to Europe's climate reduction policy on aviation emissions. There were calls during the meeting for re-engagement and accelerated action by ICAO towards a global agreement on market-based measures for emissions mitigation.

[30] US stiffens opposition to European carbon emissions ruling, *Airletter*, Thursday 07 June, No. 17,498 at p. 2.

[31] Lawmakers to Urge Action on Article 84 Complaint to Challenge ETS, *Aviation Daily*, March 29 2012 p. 1. Article 84 of the Chicago Convention provides: "If any disagreement between two or more contracting States relating to the interpretation or application of this Convention and its Annexes cannot be settled by negotiation, it shall, on the application of any State concerned in the disagreement, be decided by the Council. No member of the Council shall vote in the consideration by the Council of any dispute to which it is a party. Any contracting State may, subject to Article 85, appeal from the decision of the Council to an ad hoc arbitral tribunal agreed upon with the other parties to the dispute or to the Permanent Court of International Justice. Any such appeal shall be notified to the Council within 60 days of receipt of notification of the decision of the Council". See *Convention on International Civil Aviation*, signed in Chicago on 7 December 1944. ICAO Doc 7300/8 8th Edition: 2006. *Supra*, 6.

economic and political issues discussed in Part One. To isolate the subject, I believe, would be nothing short of folly.

I might also add that the States opposed to the EU ETS may anchor themselves on two facts: Principle 12 of the 1992 Rio Declaration on Environment and Development states:

> …Unilateral actions to deal with environmental challenges outside the jurisdiction of the importing country should be avoided. Environmental measures addressing transboundary or global environmental problems should, as far as possible, be based on international consensus.[32]

Member States of ICAO, at the Organization's 36th Session of the Assembly (Montreal, 18–28 September 2007) adopted Resolution A36-22,[33] which, in Appendix A declares that ICAO is the lead United Nations Agency in matters involving international aviation,[34] and urges ICAO member States, in Appendix L not to implement an emissions trading system on other member States' aircraft operators except on the basis of mutual agreement between those States.[35] It is encouraging that the formal EU position with regard to ICAO is that ICAO is the natural forum to develop a global solution.[36] Mr. Daniel Calleja, Air Transport Director at the European Commission, in an interview with the *ICAO Journal* has stated that the EU is committed to processes that have been launched by ICAO's GIACC. Mr.Calleja also stated at the same interview that the EU is ready to change its position if a more global solution can be agreed upon.[37] This could be the ultimate approach for a globally acceptable trading mechanism.

Now that the ball was clearly on ICAO's Court the Organization started examining a series of options to proceed with. The first option was to recommend a carbon offsetting scheme that would use 2020 as a baseline. The basis of this framework was that if an airline operator emitted CO_2 in excess of its allocated amount it would have to purchase carbon credits. Ex facie this does not seem any different from the fundamental principle of emissions trading except that the ICAO model would be globally applicable, which meant that the reporting, monitoring and verification of an airline's emissions activity would have to be done on a global basis.

The second ICAO option seemed to be an offsetting scheme combined with extra revenue. In addition to an offsetting cost, as envisioned in the first option, this version would also entail a cost in relation to the amount of credits being

---

[32] http://www.jus.uio.no/lm/environmental.development.rio.declaration.1992/12.html.

[33] Consolidated statement of continuing ICAO policies and practices related to environmental protection, *Assembly Resolutions in Force* (As of 28 September 2007), ICAO Doc 9902, 1–54 to 1–74.

[34] Id, Appendix A, at 1–55.

[35] Id. Appendix L, at 1–73.

[36] Striving Toward Meaningful Solutions, an Interview with Mr. Daniel Calleja, *ICAO Journal*, Issue 04, 2008 14–15 at 15.

[37] Ibid.

purchased. All this would of course be subject to international criteria and much would depend on the quantum of the extra revenue involved.

The third option being considered by ICAO is a global ETS scheme much along the lines of the EU ETS but on a global level that would not entail issues of extra territoriality and infringements of sovereignty as claimed by the many detractors of the EU ETS. The critical issue here would be the manner in which the money raised by this scheme would be utilized. Therein lies the entire answer to this thorny issue. ICAO was to deliver a final scheme, replete with explanations and details, at the 38th Session of its Assembly (to be held in September/October 2013), which meant that the Council would have to approve such a scheme in toto at least by December 2012.[38]

Those working on developing an ICAO global framework (called the Ad hoc Working Group on Market Based Measures—which includes a working group comprised of members of the ICAO Secretariat and representatives from key stakeholders, such as IATA) explained to the ICAO Council at an informal briefing given in June 2012 that ICAO's approach would be based on six key areas: infrastructure (which would take into account NextGen and SESAR[39]) operations; retrofitting or reequipping existing aircraft; biofuels; fleet structures; and estimated impact of biofuels. The ultimate scheme presented to the world would introduce market based measures(MBMs) as economic measures and policy tools that would provide participants flexibility while offering incentives to low cost reductions of emissions. These MBMs, which would be put in force simultaneously with infrastructure and operations, would ensure that carbon neutral growth is achieved through their application.

Market Based Measures (MBMs)

Emissions trading is one of many market based measures. As ICAO states: market-based measures include: emissions trading, emission related levies—charges and taxes, and emissions offsetting; all of which aim to contribute to the achievement of specific environmental goals, at a lower cost, and in a more flexible manner, than traditional command and control regulatory measures. Market-based measures are among the elements of a comprehensive mitigation strategy to address greenhouse gas (GHG) emissions from international aviation that are being considered by ICAO.[40]

---

[38] A World of Difference—Solutions to the European Union Emissions Trading Controversy...*Airlines International*, Issue 38 June (IATA) AGM 2012 at 62.

[39] For a discussion on NextGen and SESAR, see (Abeyratne 2012c).

[40] http://www.icao.int/environmental-protection/Pages/market-based-measures.aspx.

A good exposé of MBMs is found in Assembly Resolution A37-19 Annex which provides the guiding principles for the design and implementation of market-based measures (MBMs) for international aviation as:

(a) MBMs should support sustainable development of the international aviation sector;
(b) MBMs should support the mitigation of GHG emissions from international aviation;
(c) MBMs should contribute towards achieving global aspirational goals;
(d) MBMs should be transparent and administratively simple;
(e) MBMs should be cost-effective;
(f) MBMs should not be duplicative and international aviation CO_2 emissions should be accounted for only once;
(g) MBMs should minimize carbon leakage and market distortions;
(h) MBMs should ensure the fair treatment of the international aviation sector in relation to other sectors;
(i) MBMs should recognize past and future achievements and investments in aviation fuel efficiency and in other measures to reduce aviation emissions;
(j) MBMs should not impose inappropriate economic burden on international aviation;
(k) MBMs should facilitate appropriate access to all carbon markets;
(l) MBMs should be assessed in relation to various measures on the basis of performance measured in terms of CO_2 emissions reductions or avoidance, where appropriate;
(m) MBMs should include *de minimis* provisions;
(n) where revenues are generated from MBMs, it is strongly recommended that they should be applied in the first instance to mitigating the environmental impact of aircraft engine emissions, including mitigation and adaptation, as well as assistance to and support for developing States; and
(o) where emissions reductions are achieved through MBMs, they should be identified in States' emissions reporting.

In November 2011, the International Monetary Fund and the World Bank, in a Report on financing climate change through levies on air and maritime transport[41] had this to say:

Market-based instruments (MBIs) for international aviation and maritime fuels—either emissions (fuel) taxes or emissions trading schemes (ETS)—have appeal as an 'innovative' source of climate finance. These activities are currently under-charged from an environmental perspective: unlike domestic transportation fuels, they are subject to no excise tax to reflect environmental damages in fuel prices. Since they correct an unpriced distortion rather than exacerbating those

---

[41] Market-Based Instruments for International Aviation and Shipping as a Source of Climate Finance, Background Paper for the Report to the G20 on—Mobilizing Sources of Climate Finance, http://www.imf.org/external/np/g20/pdf/110411a.pdf at p.

from pre-existing taxes, MBIs for jet and international marine fuels are likely a much more cost-effective way to raise finance for climate (or other) purposes than are broader fiscal instruments.

By 2020, a globally implemented carbon charge of $25 per tonne of CO_2 on these fuels could raise around $12 billion from international aviation and around $26 billion for shipping, while moderately reducing CO_2 emissions from each sector by reducing fuel demand. Once in place, presumably the fuel charges would increase gradually over time to promote more aggressive emissions mitigation.

Compensating developing States for the economic harm they might suffer from such charges—ensuring that they bear 'no net incidence'—is widely recognized as critical to their acceptability. Such compensation seems to require—at most— 40 % of global revenues, which would leave about $23 billion or more for climate finance or other uses.[42]

References

Abeyratne R (2011) Aviation and the carbon trade. Nova Science Publishers, New York
Abeyratne R (2012a) Aeronomics and law—fixing anomalies. Springer, Heidelberg (Chapter Two)
Abeyratne R (2012b) Strategic issues in air transport—legal, economic and technical issues. Springer, Heidelberg, pp 279–318
Abeyratne R (2012c) Air navigation law. Springer, Heidelberg, pp 221–228
Hubbert MK (1949) Energy from fossil fuels. Science 109:103
Monbiot G (2006) Heat: how to stop the planet from burning. Doubleday, Canada (at Introduction p. xvii)

---

[42] Id. p. 5.

Chapter 4
The Challenge Faced by ICAO

Introduction

Climate change is no longer a theory and has fast become an unequivocal reality and a defining issue of our time. Its enormity can be identified numerically. For instance 2005 was the warmest year on record. There has been a 33 % rise in global carbon dioxide emissions since 1987. The Inter-Governmental Panel on Climate Change (IPCC) records that 5 million extra people are at risk of hunger by the year 2020 if climate change continues unabated. The 2003 heat wave killed 35,000 people in Europe. Environmental campaigner Sheila Watt-Cloutier, in her article "A Human Issue" in the May 2007 issue of *"Our Planet"*—the magazine of the United Nations Environment Programme, says that there are palpable signs of drastic climate change in the Arctic, which she calls the health barometer for the planet. Whatever happens in the world occurs first in the Arctic—the home of Inuit. In 2004 certain conclusions were reached by the Arctic Climate Impact Assessment (ACIA) as a result of work carried out by 300 scientists from 15 countries. Among the results, according to Watt-Cloutier, is that for Inuit, warming is likely to disrupt or even destroy their hunting and food-sharing culture as reduced sea ice causes populations to decline or become extinct. The Inuit have lived in the arctic for thousands of years and their culture and economy reflect their homeland. Climate change in the arctic would therefore infringe the basic human right of the Inuit to life.

In the same issue of *Our Planet*, Basanta Shresta, in his article "Mountain Tsunamis" states that glaziers are retreating in the face of accelerating global warming, as human activities cause steadily increasing concentrations of greenhouse gases in the atmosphere and their melting is an important indicator of climate change. This is confirmed by the Fourth Assessment Report of the IPCC, released in the first half of 2007, which records that most of the observed increase in global averaged temperatures since the mid 20th century is very likely due to the observed increase in anthropogenic greenhouse gas concentrations. According to

© The Author(s) 2014
R. Abeyratne, *Aviation and Climate Change*, SpringerBriefs in Law,
DOI: 10.1007/978-3-319-08443-5_4

the Report, rising temperatures in the Arctic have caused a decline of 2.7 % of sea ice since 1978. A third of the glazier surface in Bolivia and Peru has disappeared since the seventies. The Report concludes that climate change is one of the most critical global challenges of our time.

The former Secretary General of the United Nations, Kofi Annan, in his Report to the Fifty Ninth Session of the UN General Assembly in March 2005, observed that one of the greatest environmental and developmental challenges in the twenty first century will be to control and cope with climate change. The Secretary General drew the attention of the General Assembly to the fact that entry into force in February 2005 of the 1997 Kyoto Protocol to the United Nations Framework Convention on Climate Change was an important step toward dealing with global warming. Since the Protocol extends only until 2012, the Secretary General called upon the international community to agree on stabilization targets for greenhouse gas concentrations beyond that date. To achieve this goal, scientific advancement and technological innovation must be mobilized for carbon management and energy efficiency, the responsibility for which lies with the countries that contribute to most of the problems.

The Third Conference of the Parties to the United Nations Framework Convention on Climate Change (Climate Change Convention) was held from to 11 December 1997 at Kyoto, Japan. Significantly the States parties to the Convention adopted a protocol (Kyoto Protocol) on 11 December 1997 under which industrialized countries have agreed to reduce their collective emissions of six greenhouse gases by at least 5 % by 2008–2012. Ambassador Raul Estrada-Oyuela, who had chaired the Committee of the Whole established by the Conference to facilitate the negotiation of a Protocol text, expressed the view that the agreement will have a real impact on the problem of greenhouse gas emissions and that 11 December 1997 should be remembered as "the Day of the Atmosphere".

The Kyoto Protocol, in Article 1 (a) (v) calls each State Party to achieve progressive or phasing out of market imperfections, fiscal incentives, tax and duty exemptions and subsidies in all greenhouse gas emitting sectors that run counter to the objective of the Convention and application of market instruments. The subject of emissions leading to trading is addressed initially in Article 3 of the Protocol which requires States Parties to ensure that their aggregate anthropogenic carbon dioxide equivalent emissions of the greenhouse gases listed in Annex A do not exceed their assigned amounts, calculated pursuant to their quantified emission limitation and reduction commitments inscribed in Annex B. The provision also requires States parties to the Protocol to reduce their overall emissions of greenhouse gases by at least 5 % below 1990 levels in the commitment period 2008–2012. Article 3 (6) goes further, in providing that States Parties shall be allowed a certain degree of flexibility in implementation of Article 3 and the reduction of their emission standards.

This approach has been endorsed by many learned and informed commentators, among whom is former US Vice President Al Gore, who in his movie "An

Inconvenient Truth" highlighted the fact that the Earth's atmosphere is thin enough that we can change its composition with the emissions we produce through industrial activity and transportation. Gore, who has dedicated his career both as a distinguished politician in the United States where he served under President Clinton as Vice President and also as an erudite academic with impressive credentials, makes the frightening but accurate claim that the vastly increasing levels of Carbon Dioxide we produce can thicken the atmosphere so that the rays of the Sun which fall on Earth and bounce back as infra red rays beyond the atmosphere cannot escape the thick atmospheric layer at the rate they did before and are trapped within, making the world warmer. This phenomenon has resulted in Carbon Dioxide being termed a greenhouse gas as it causes a greenhouse effect by retaining heat within the atmosphere.

The environmental crisis that we face now is that the solar energy that we receive from the Sun, which under normal circumstances and for years has been retained in quantities that benefit the Earth in terms of the balance of its ecosystem and biodiversity, and the rest released by way of infra red rays, is not being released as it should as more infra red rays are being trapped due to the Carbon Dioxide induced layer surrounding the atmosphere. Popularly called "global warming" this phenomenon is the result of the observed increase in the average temperature of the Earth's atmosphere and oceans in recent decades. It is claimed that the Earth's average near-surface atmospheric temperature rose 0.6 ± 0.2 °C (1.1 ± 0.4 °F) in the 20th century. The current scientific consensus is that most of the observed warming over the last 50 years is likely to have been attributable to human activities. As already stated, the main cause of the human-induced component of warming is the increase in atmospheric greenhouse gases (GHGs), especially Carbon Dioxide (CO_2), due to activities such as burning of fossil fuels, land clearing, and agriculture. Greenhouse gases are gases that contribute to the greenhouse effect. This effect was first described by Joseph Fourier in 1824, and was first investigated quantitatively in 1896 by the Swedish Chemist Svante Arhenius.

Another vocal commentator is George Monbiot, a radical thinker and visiting professor at Oxford Brookes University, who claims in his book "*HEAT: How to Stop the Planet from Burning*", that if in the year 2030, carbon dioxide concentrations in the atmosphere remain as high as they are today, the likely result is an increase of two degrees warming above pre-industrial levels, which is the point beyond which certain major ecosystems begin collapsing. The collapse of one's environment would eventually bring about catastrophic results and threaten human existence. When this prospect is viewed in the context of human rights, climate change, and our apathy toward it would infringe our basic right to life, as in the case of Inuit cited above.

The basic protection of human rights starts at the least desirable level of existence. Although this is a minimalist approach, it is arguably the best starting point and perhaps the only one we have. A right is something due to a person by just claim, legal guarantee or moral principle. It is a power, privilege or immunity accrued to a person by law and is a legally enforceable claim that another will do or will not do a given act. It is also a recognized and protected interest, the violation of which is wrong. Therefore, the starting point should be in the words "just claim" "legal guarantee" and "moral principle". These claims and guarantees based on moral principles should be justiciable.

The question now is, how could we enforce the human right to life and ensure that life is not jeopardized by continued climate change? The first step of course would be to recognize the enormity of climate change. The second is to enforce measures.

Being already aware of this trend, Ryanair, known to be Europe's greenest airline, is investing some E 17 billion on its fleet replacement and expansion programme which began in 1999. All of Ryanair's older Boeing 737–200 aircraft have already been replaced with next generation 737–800 aircraft, which has made Ryanair the airline with the youngest and most modern fleet in all of Europe. These measures put Ryanair in the forefront as an airline which minimises and continues to reduce fuel burn and carbon dioxide emissions per passenger kilometre. The low cost business model used by Rayanair (and other low cost carriers) which involves the use of secondary airports with no holding patterns as in busier airports and point to point services (which eliminate multiple landings) help increase fuel efficiency and restrict emissions. It is reported that Ryanair's fleet replacement has resulted in an overall reduction in fuel consumption of 52 % between 1998 and 2006.

On the other side of the Atlantic, American Airlines, with one of the largest fleets in the world, is also involved in a comprehensive aircraft weight-reduction program. The airline has removed ovens and galleys from aircraft on which hot food is not served. It also carries less potable water on flights. Although earlier it was routine for maintenance personnel to simply fill the water tanks prior to flight, a study conducted by the airline revealed that usually less than half the water was being consumed. Following this realization, the maintenance department designed a $1 valve that shuts off the filler hose when the tank reaches 75 % capacity rather than change the water-tank filling procedure, which resulted in a reduction of aircraft weight by about 100 pounds and a saving of approximately $2.8 million in fuel annually.

Carbon offsetting is one way of mitigating the effects of climate change. This act of mitigating ("offsetting") greenhouse gas emissions is well exemplified by the simple exercise of planting of trees to compensate for the greenhouse gas emissions from personal air travel.

A wide variety of offset methods are in use—while tree planting has initially been a mainstay of carbon offsetting, renewable energy and energy conservation offsets are now becoming increasingly popular. Carbon offsetting as part of a "carbon neutral" lifestyle has gained some appeal and momentum mainly among consumers in western countries who have become aware and concerned about the potentially negative effects of energy-demanding lifestyles and economies on the environment. The Kyoto Protocol has sanctioned official offsets for governments and private companies to earn carbon credits which can be traded on a marketplace. This has contributed to the increasing popularity of voluntary offsets among private individuals and also companies. Offsets may be cheaper or more convenient alternatives to reducing one's own fossil-fuel consumption. However, some critics object to carbon offsets, and many have questioned the benefits of certain types of offsets (such as tree planting), and other projects.

If climate change can ultimately decide whether a human has the right to live, and it indeed can, the whole issue must be approached on the basis of social and moral principles applicable to human rights. There must be global enforcement of measures such as carbon offsets and emissions trading. Alternative fuels should be considered a necessary alternative to fossil fuels. These measures must be taken through a global forum which is inevitably the United Nations. The United Nations is all about "nations". Nations are people, as against countries which are defined geographic areas, and States which are a collection of agencies that form a government. Therefore human rights should incontrovertibly be about nations and their interactions and people helping one another. Rights are generated through human experience, particularly with injustice. Therefore, although such rights are technically entrenched in a Bill of Rights or Constitution, they should not be limited to the law that is written down but be extended whenever required to include new rights if an injustice or wrong is about to be committed.

The Committee on Aviation Environmental Protection (CAEP)[1] of the Council of ICAO held its seventh meeting (CAEP/7) in Montreal from 5 to 16 February 2007, following an year designated the *International Year for Deserts and*

---

[1] ICAO's current environmental activities are largely undertaken through the Committee on Aviation Environmental Protection (CAEP), which was established by the Council in 1983, superseding the Committee on Aircraft Noise (CAN) and the Committee on Aircraft Engine Emissions (CAEE). CAEP is composed of members and observers. In 1998, the Assembly requested that States from regions that are not represented or under-represented in CAEP participate in the Committee's work. Some progress has been made in this regard and efforts continue to attract new participants. CAEP assists the Council in formulating new policies and adopting new Standards on aircraft noise and aircraft engine emissions. CAEP's Terms of Reference and Work Programme are established by the Council. The current structure of the Committee includes five working groups and one support group. Two of the working groups deal with the technical and operational aspects of noise reduction and mitigation. The other three working groups deal with technical and operational aspects of aircraft emissions, and with the study of market-based measures to limit or reduce emissions such as emissions trading, emissions-related charges and voluntary measures. The support group provides information on the economic costs and environmental benefits of the noise and emissions options considered by CAEP.

Desertification by the United Nations. 2006 was an year in which environmentalists made the frightening but accurate claim that the vastly increasing levels of Carbon Dioxide we produce can thicken the atmosphere so that the rays of the Sun which fall on Earth and bounce back as infra red rays beyond the atmosphere cannot escape the thick atmospheric layer at the rate they did before and are trapped within, making the world warmer.

One of the major issues addressed by CAEP/7 was emissions trading, resulting in guidelines presented by CAEP to the ICAO Council, which will in turn be presented to the 36th Session of the ICAO Assembly in September 2007 for consideration by ICAO's 190 member States. In this regard a major contribution to CAEP/7 was a proposal presented by the European Commission calculated to include aviation activities in the scheme of greenhouse gas emission allowance trading within the Community. From a legal perspective, such a proposal would present issues that would attract discussion on perspectives of international law and policy. This article discusses the CAEP/7 Guidelines and the EC Policy against the backdrop of applicable principles of public and customary international law.

It is said that the Earth's atmosphere is so thin that we have the capacity to dramatically alter the concentration of some of its basic molecular components (Gore 2006). With this ability we have vastly increased the amount of carbon dioxide (CO_2)—the most important of the so called "greenhouse gases"(GHGs)[2] that contribute to the greenhouse effect.[3] The increase in greenhouse gases, particularly CO_2 gases, causes global warming which threatens the ecosystem and causes alterations of weather. With the warming of the Earth, even by moderate levels, sea levels could increase by some 40 cm and the number of people endangered by floods with the rise in sea level could go up from 75 million today to around 250 million.[4] The rise in sea level could also pollute the drinking water in cities such as Shanghai, Manila, Jakarta, Bangkok, Kolkota, Mumbai, Karachi, Lagos, Buenos Aires and Lima.[5]

It is reported that the West Antarctic ice sheet could, if it does melt as a result of global warming, raise the sea level that could flood parts of New York, London, Tokyo and Mumbai (Monbiot 2006). This looks ominously real in the face of the

---

[2] Greenhouse gases are components of the atmosphere and contribute to the Greenhouse Effect (*infra.*, note 331). Some greenhouse gases occur naturally in the atmosphere, while others result from human activities. Naturally occurring greenhouse gases include water vapor, carbon dioxide, methane, nitrous oxide, and ozone. Certain human activities add to the levels of most of these naturally occurring gases.

[3] When sunlight reaches the surface of earth, some of it is absorbed and warms the earth. Because the Earth's surface is much cooler than the sun, it radiates energy at much longer wavelengths than the sun. Some energy in these longer wavelengths is absorbed by greenhouse gases in the atmosphere before it can be lost to space. The absorption of this longwave radiant energy warms the atmosphere, which is called the Greenhouse Effect.

[4] IPCC 2001 Working Group II, *Impacts, Adaptation and Vulnerability* http:// www.grida.no/ climate/ipcc_tar/wg2/005.htm.

[5] Conference of the International Association of Hydrologists, reported by Fred Pearce, Cities May be Abandoned as Salt Water Invades, *New Scientist*, 16 April 2005 at 2.

fact that in 2003 Europe was hit by a massive heat wave that killed 35,000 people and 2005 was the hottest year recorded during the period 1860–2005.[6]

It was against this backdrop that the Committee on Aviation Environmental Protection (CAEP)—a technical group of experts forming a committee of the Council of ICAO held its seventh meeting (CAEP/7) in Montreal from 5 to 16 February 2007 to respond to the decision of the 35th Session of the ICAO Assembly, held in September/October 2004 which encouraged States and other parties involved to limit or reduce international aviation emissions through voluntary measures and urged the Council to facilitate actions by making available guidelines that ICAO had developed for such measures.[7]

When it comes to debate on economic measures for aircraft engine emissions the rhetoric in the ICAO Council has always been about politics and not about statesmanship. The so called developing States have militated against any constraints being placed on them on the ground that they should have untrammelled opportunity for development as did the developed States 50 years ago. Against this backdrop, the global response to climate change is bifurcated into mitigation and adaptation. Mitigation (also called abatement) is human intervention to reduce the sources of greenhouse gases. Adaptation is adjustments in practices, processes or structure that takes into consideration the vicissitudes of climate change. Against this backdrop, the investor has certain choices: accept the scientific evidence and invest in industries that help mitigate climate change; take no action and consider scientific evidence as irrelevant and unnecessary; or look for investment opportunities, taking into account government initiatives. The last option is vigorously espoused by international organizations with the active involvement of governments. International organizations will most likely continue to demand initiatives that mitigate climate change through governmental intervention. Such government initiatives are already visible in the form of cap and trade regulatory systems, taxes in various forms, incentives and subsidies and standardization for energy efficiency.

---

[6] AL Gore, supra. note 174 at 73. Gore goes on to say that science textbooks had to be re-written in 2004. They used to say "It's impossible to have hurricanes in the South Atlantic." But that year, a hurricane hit Brazil. *Id.* 84.

[7] It must be noted that the 33rd ICAO Assembly held in 2001 endorsed the development of an open emissions trading system for international aviation and requested the Council to develop, as a matter of priority, the guidelines for open emissions trading for international aviation, focusing on establishing the structural and legal basis for aviation's participation in an open trading system, and including key elements, such as reporting, monitoring and compliance, while providing flexibility to the maximum extent possible consistent with the United Nations Framework Convention on Climate Change (UNFCCC or FCCC).

Subsequently, at its 35th Assembly session, held in 2004, ICAO endorsed the further development of an open emissions trading system for international aviation and requested the Council, in its further work on this subject, to focus on two approaches, namely to support the development of a voluntary trading system that interesting Contracting States and international organizations might propose and to provide guidance for use by member States, as appropriate, to incorporate emissions from international aviation into member States emissions trading Schemes consistent with the UNFCC process.

In 2013, at the 38th Session of the ICAO Assembly, things came to a head in the international aviation community where more than 170 member States and numerous international Organizations pledged to develop a global Market Based Measures Scheme at the next session of the Assembly in 2016. Both ICAO and the international aviation community had been kicking the can down the road for more than a decade. It was time for concrete action. This article addresses the complexities, sensibilities and possibilities of developing a global MBM scheme

Not many, and certainly no one that I know in the aviation industry, has talked about anything other than the effects economic measures taken to counter the growing threat of climate change would have on the developmental progress of their country. Often the larger picture that portends the devastation climate change would bring the world is shrouded in polemics on equity based on the right to development. This trend has obfuscated the catastrophe facing mankind, not only in terms of rising sea levels, skinny polar bears and parched wheat fields, but also in the threat to human life as a result of an increasingly warming planet. The World Health Organization has come up with the fact that, over the past 30 years, 150,000 people annually have died as a result of global warming (Marsa 2013). A commentator says:

> The wild swings in the weather that are expected to become commonplace on a warmer planet—more frequent and severe droughts followed by drenching rains—also change ecosystems in a way that awakens and expedites the transmission of once-dormant pathogens. The emergence of hantavirus pulmonary syndrome, a spread by rodents, is a good example.[8]

Yet, with all these revelations and incontrovertible facts, the debate on aircraft engine emissions and what to do about them remains an exclusively economic issue based on pollution as a by-product of development.

At the 38th Session of the ICAO Assembly, convened in Montreal from 24 September to 4 October 2013, the most contentious issue under discussion was market based measures in aviation and the environment. So it was at the preceding session of the Assembly in 2010. The 38th Session barely managed to agree by consensus that, by the 39th session of the Assembly in 2016, ICAO would come up with a proposal for a global market based "scheme" that would enable the industry to achieve carbon neutral growth in 2020 and at the same time, apply a global standard for addressing aircraft engine emissions. ICAO placed on its website the following statement after the conclusion of the Assembly session:

> ICAO's States agreed to report back in 2016 with a proposal for a global MBM scheme capable of being implemented by 2020. Major efforts will need to be undertaken in order to address the challenges and accommodate specific concerns of developing States going forward.[9]

---

[8] *Id.* 39.

[9] http://www.icao.int/meetings/a38/Pages/default.aspx.

The International Air Transport Association,[10] in its press release issued after the Assembly session called the proposed market based scheme a market based "measure" (my emphasis).[11] Although it is not clear whether these nomenclatures are one and the same, what is clear is that 3 years earlier, at the 37th Session of the Assembly, more or less the same result was expected of the 38th Session which seems now to have kicked the can down the road for another 3 years. The 37th Session, in Resolution A37-19[12] required ICAO to develop a framework for market-based measures while attaining global aspirations in the reduction of emissions taking into consideration *inter alia* the maturity of aviation markets and the sustainable growth of the international aviation industry. Although the Resolution on the one hand only required its recommendations to be reviewed at the 38th Session in 2013 there was an explicit requirement in resolving clause 13 of the Resolution that the Council, with the support of member States, undertake work to develop a framework for market-based measures (MBMs) in international aviation.

Resolution A37-19, which in essence contained ICAO's mandate to deliver a framework of market based measures to the 38th session of the Assembly in 2013 had clear guidelines. Additionally, the Resolution prescribed that such a framework should be the outcome of in-depth study and consideration of special circumstances and respective capabilities of developing States against the backdrop of processes and mechanisms to facilitate the provision of technical and financial assistance, as well as facilitate access to existing and new financial resources, technology transfer and capacity building, to developing States; it should take into account respective capabilities and contribution of States to the concentration of aviation greenhouse gas (GHG) emissions in the atmosphere; the maturity of aviation markets; and the sustainable growth of the international

---

[10] The International Air Transport Association, an association of air carriers, was formed in 1919 as the International Air Traffic Association. Encapsulated in IATA's overall mission are seven core objectives: to promote safe, reliable and secure air services; to achieve recognition of the importance of a healthy air transport industry to worldwide social and economic development; to assist the air transport industry in achieving adequate levels of profitability; to provide high quality, value for money, industry-required products and services that meet the needs of the customer; to develop cost effective, environmentally-friendly standards and procedures to facilitate the operation of international air transport; to identify and articulate common industry positions and support the resolution of key industry issues; and to provide a working environment which attracts, retains and develops committed employees.

[11] ICAO defines "market based measures" inclusively as composed of emissions trading, emission related levies—charges and taxes, and emissions offsetting; all of which aim to contribute to the achievement of specific environmental goals, at a lower cost, and in a more flexible manner, than traditional command and control regulatory measures. Market-based measures are among the elements of a comprehensive mitigation strategy to address greenhouse gas (GHG) emissions from international aviation that are being considered by ICAO. See http://www.icao.int/environmental-protection/Pages/market-based-measures.aspx.

[12] A37-19: Consolidated statement of continuing ICAO policies and practices related to environmental protection—Climate Change, Annex. See Assembly Resolutions (as of 8 October 2010), ICAO: 2011, 1–67 at 1–73.

aviation industry. All these factors were brought into focus in the Resolution by the driving force that is the vital role which international aviation plays in global economic and social development and the need to ensure that international aviation continues to develop in a sustainable manner.[13]

The "framework" which was required for discussion at the 38th Session of the Assembly was presented by the ICAO Council in the form of three options: They were:

(a) global mandatory offsetting, where participants acquire emissions units to offset emissions from international aviation above an agreed baseline;
(b) global mandatory offsetting complemented by a revenue generation mechanism would generally function the same way as the mandatory offsetting scheme. A key difference would be that in addition to offsetting, revenue would be generated by applying a fee to each tonne of carbon, for instance, through a transaction fee. The revenue would be used for agreed purposes, such as climate change mitigation or providing support to developing States to reduce GHG emissions; and
(c) global emissions trading scheme using a cap and trade approach, where total international aviation emissions are capped at an agreed level for a specified compliance period. Aviation allowances (one allowance is equivalent to one tonne of CO_2) would be created for all the emissions under the cap. These allowances would then be distributed among, or auctioned to, participants, using an agreed method. At the end of each compliance period, participants would need to surrender sufficient aviation allowances, or other emissions units, such as offsets from other sectors, to cover all the emissions generated during that period. Revenues can be generated by auctioning aviation allowances.[14]

These options were accepted by the 38th Session of the ICAO Assembly, which adopted Resolution A38-18 (Consolidated statement of continuing ICAO policies and practices related to environmental protection—climate change) and set parameters (identical to those which were set at the 37th session of the Assembly) within which market based measures should be considered over the next 3 years. They are:

(a) MBMs should support sustainable development of the international aviation sector;
(b) MBMs should support the mitigation of GHG emissions from international aviation;
(c) MBMs should contribute towards achieving global aspirational goals;
(d) MBMs should be transparent and administratively simple;
(e) MBMs should be cost-effective;

---

[13] For an in-depth discussion on Resolution A37-19 and market based measures see Ruwantissa Abeyratne, Aircraft Emissions—In Search of a Global Framework for Market Based Measures, *Issues in Aviation Law and Policy,* Vol. 12.1 (2012), 7–46.

[14] A38-WP/29, EX/24, 4/09/13 at 2.

(f) MBMs should not be duplicative and international aviation CO_2 emissions should be accounted for only once;

(g) MBMs should minimize carbon leakage and market distortions;

(h) MBMs should ensure the fair treatment of the international aviation sector in relation to other sectors;

(i) MBMs should recognize past and future achievements and investments in aviation fuel efficiency and in other measures to reduce aviation emissions;

(j) MBMs should not impose inappropriate economic burden on international aviation;

(k) MBMs should facilitate appropriate access to all carbon markets;

(l) MBMs should be assessed in relation to various measures on the basis of performance measured in terms of CO_2 emissions reductions or avoidance, where appropriate;

(m) MBMs should include *de minimis* provisions;

(n) where revenues are generated from MBMs, it is strongly recommended that they should be applied in the first instance to mitigating the environmental impact of aircraft engine emissions, including mitigation and adaptation, as well as assistance to and support for developing States; and

(o) where emissions reductions are achieved through MBMs, they should be identified in States' emissions reporting.

Of these two areas of global relevance stood out at the 38th Session of the Assembly: They are the Common but Differentiated Responsibility (CBDR) principle which should be applied along with regard to Special Circumstances and Respective Capabilities (SCRC) of developing States, and the *de minimis* provisions. According to the CBDR principle, every State has the common responsibility to protect the environment but the responsibilities they shoulder in attaining this objective may differ and vary according to their economic, social and ecological situations. In other words, this principle places more responsibility on wealthier industrialized States which could contribute more toward climate change and global warming than developing States. The CBDR principle is based on equity, which is a common law set of legal principles that supplement strict rules of law where the application of such rules would operate harshly. Equity is commonly said to "mitigate the rigor of common law", allowing courts to use their discretion and apply justice in accordance with natural law.

The CBDR principle's legitimacy is enshrined in Principle 7 of the Rio Declaration[15] which provides:

> States shall cooperate in a spirit of global partnership to conserve, protect and restore the health and integrity of the Earth's ecosystem. In view of the different contributions to global environmental degradation, States have common but differentiated responsibilities. The developed States acknowledge the responsibility that they bear in the international pursuit to sustainable development in view of the pressures their societies place on the global environment and of the technologies and financial resources they command.

---

[15] 1992 Rio Declaration on Environment and Development, 31 ILM 874 (1992).

Some States[16] at the Assembly, while asserting that MBMs should abide by the principle of CBDR and the principle of SCRC demanded that SCRC should be restricted only to 'developing States'. They also demanded that ICAO assess and evaluate the feasibility and practicability of a global MBM scheme for international aviation with member States, taking into account the views of all States of ICAO, and also address concerns on the impact of such a scheme on all sectors. In this context, they requested that all States of ICAO submit their views as to the feasibility and practicability to the Council before such assessment and evaluation is completed and any MBM, before it is considered feasible and practicable. States should also take into account common but differentiated responsibilities and the special circumstances and respective capabilities of developing States, while minimizing market distortions.[17]

With regard to the *de minimis* principle the same States requested the Council to review the *de minimis* principle, including the *de minimis* threshold of MBMs, taking into account the specific circumstances of States and potential impacts on the international aviation industry and markets, and with regard to the guiding principles listed in (a)–(o) above, to be presented for consideration by the 39th Session of the Assembly in 2016. The threshold quoted was;

(a) in 2014, 1 % 4,700,000,000 of total revenue ton kilometres (RTK) of international civil aviation activities, until the global scheme is decided; and

(b) after 2014, a threshold that is reduced by 470,000,000 RTK each year.[18]

Herein lies the problem. It is one thing to resolve, yet again, after assiduous studies and consultation by ICAO for 3 years between 2010 and 2013, that in the next 3 years to come, ICAO will come up with a globally applicable market based scheme that could apply from 2020. It is completely another thing to expect all 191 member States of ICAO to agree to such a scheme if it does not accord with developing States' issues on CBDR, SCRC and the *de minimis* thresholds.

Yet another worrying fact is that the valid and reasonable request of member States of the European Union (and the European Civil Aviation Conference—ECAC)—whose contentious inclusion of aviation in its emissions trading scheme[19] was the primary cause of the discussion on a globally acceptable and

---

[16] Argentina, Brazil, China, Cuba, India, Islamic Republic of Iran, Pakistan, Peru, Russian Federation, Saudi Arabia, South Africa.

[17] A38-WP/432 EX/144 01/10/13, at 2.

[18] A38-WP/425 EX/140 01/10/13, at 2.

[19] In 2008, the European Union amended its Emissions Trading Scheme to include the aviation sector. Initially, in 2011, only flights between EU airports were to be included in the Scheme. From 2012, this was extended to all flights arriving at or departing from an EU airport. This meant that the ETS became applicable to any airline and its flights that are destined to Europe from anywhere in the world, and vice versa. Convention. the Scheme would apply, for example, to a U.S. carrier's entire flight from New York to London, covering, *inter alia*, emissions released over American airspace and over other territorial airspace before entering European airspace. Detractors of ETS claim that this is an extraterritorial application of European law. See Abeyratne, *Aeronomics and Law—Fixing Anomalies*, *supra* note 82 at 8–9.

applicable MBM, for a work programme to develop such an MBM, was totally ignored by the Assembly. The EU/ECAC member States' request was that the Assembly should agree to the implementation of a global MBM for application by 2020, and should therefore adopt a work programme and timetable for completing the design of the global MBM at the 38th ICAO Assembly. Member States of EU/ECAC suggested that this work programme should consist of a set of tasks to deliver the key technical elements for endorsement at the 39th ICAO Assembly in 2016, including means to take into account the special circumstances and respective capabilities of States, in ways that are non-discriminatory between aircraft operators and minimise risks of market distortion.[20]

In the absence of such diligence and strategic thinking, it is difficult to imagine how ICAO would plod its way through what has proved to be an impossible task. On the other hand, ICAO could always anchor itself in defence when the time comes in 2016, that, as it stated in its website, the Organization was only asked to "to report back in 2016 with a proposal for a global MBM scheme capable of being implemented by 2020".[21] It will not be difficult to come up with a "proposal" after in 3 years of deliberation.

The Delicate Balance

The Resolution

The Assembly resolved that, States and relevant Organizations will work through ICAO to achieve a global annual average fuel efficiency improvement efficiency of 2 percent until 2020 and an aspirational global fuel efficiency improvement rate of 2 % per annum from 2021 to 2050, calculated on the basis of volume of fuel used per revenue tonne kilometre performed.[22] By implication, therefore, whatever market based "scheme" that would be developed and placed before the 39th session of the Assembly in 2016 would have to ensure that this goal, particularly from 2020 onwards is achieved. The Council of ICAO was requested by the Assembly to exercise continuous leadership on environmental issues relating to international civil aviation, including GHG emissions and to continue to study policy options to limit or reduce the environmental impact of aircraft engine emissions and to develop "concrete proposals" (my emphasis) *inter alia* to the

---

[20] A38-WP/83 EX/38 31/7/13, at 3.

[21] *Supra*, Preface.

[22] Executive Committee's Report to the Plenary of the Assembly, A38-WP/430, P/44, 3/10/13.

Conference of the Parties (COP) of the UNFCC,[23] encompassing technical solutions and market based measures, and taking into account potential implications of such measures for developing as well as developed States.

It is worthy of note that the Resolution requires that the aspirational goal up to 2020 was to be achieved with collaborative work between ICAO, international Organizations and member States, taking into consideration SCRC of States, in particular developing States; the maturity of aviation markets; the sustainable growth of the aviation industry; and the exponential growth of air traffic.

As for the development of new MBMs and implementation of existing MBMs the Assembly resolved that international aviation should engage in constructive bilateral and/or multilateral consultations and negotiations with other States to reach an agreement and grant exemptions for application of MBMs on routes to and from developing States whose share of international civil aviation activities is below the threshold of 1 % of total revenue ton kilometres of civil aviation activities, until the global scheme is implemented. The Council was requested by the Assembly to review the *de minimis*, including *de minimis* threshold of MBMs mentioned above taking into account specific circumstances of States and potential impacts on the aviation industry and markets, and with regard to the guiding principles listed in the Annex to the Resolution, to be presented for consideration by the 39th Session of the Assembly in 2016.

Against this vast canvas and backdrop, the Assembly decided (without handing the task to the Council) to develop (not adopt) a global MBM scheme for international civil aviation taking into account work carried out by the Council *inter alia* in identifying the major issues and problems, including for member States, and make a recommendation on a global MBM scheme that appropriately addresses them and key design elements, including a means to take into account SCRC and the mechanisms for the implementation of the scheme from 2020 as part of a basket of measures which also include technologies, operational improvements and sustainable alternative fuels to achieve ICAO's aspirational goals. This work has to be reported to the 39th session of the Assembly.

One of the guidelines given by the Assembly to the Council of ICAO is that SCRC of developing States could be accommodated through *de minimis* exemptions from, or phased implementation for the application of an MBM to particular

---

[23] The United Nations Framework Convention on Climate Change (UNFCCC) was adopted on 9 May 1992 and the treaty entered into force on 21 March 1994. The UNFCCC or FCCC is an international environmental treaty produced at the United Nations Conference on Environment and Development (UNCED), informally known as the Earth Summit, held in Rio de Janeiro in 1992. The treaty aimed at reducing emissions of greenhouse gas in order to combat global warming. The treaty as originally framed set no mandatory limits on greenhouse gas emissions for individual nations and contained no enforcement provisions; it is therefore considered legally non-binding. Rather, the treaty included provisions for updates (called "protocols") that would set mandatory emission limits. The principal update is the Kyoto Protocol, which has become much better known than the UNFCCC itself. The stated objective of UNFCCC is "to achieve stabilization of greenhouse gas concentrations in the atmosphere at a low enough level to prevent dangerous anthropogenic interference with the climate system."

routes or markets with low levels of international aviation activity, particularly those serving developing States. A salient feature of the Resolution is its requirement that, to the extent that the implementation of an MBM generates revenues, such revenues should be applied in the first instance to mitigating the environmental impact of aircraft engine emissions, including mitigation and adaptation, as well as assistance to and support for developing States.

Taken literally, the following conclusions can be drawn from the Resolution:

(a) It is the Assembly that will develop a global MBM scheme (presumably at its 39th Session in 2016);

(b) A scheme is defined as a plan, design, or program of action to be followed. Ironically, as discussed earlier in this article, EU and ECAC asked for just that, to be approved by the Assembly, which evaded the attention of the Assembly. The request has been pushed back for another 3 years to be considered by the 39th session of the Assembly;

(c) In order for the Assembly to embark on this task and complete it, the Council has to identify the major issues and problems, including for member States, report work done to the next Assembly and make a recommendation on a global MBM scheme;

(d) In view of the vast array of considerations involved in developing such a scheme, emissions trading is just one MBM and does not stand isolated and other MBMs will have to be given in-depth consideration as well[24]; and

(e) An MBM scheme should benefit all concerned, and therefore, there have to be trade-offs, particularly taking into consideration SCRC of States, in particular developing States; the maturity of aviation markets; the sustainable growth of the aviation industry; and the exponential growth of air traffic.

Issues of Concern

At the end of the Assembly Session, ICAO put up a brave front, making out to the world that the Resolution broke important new ground and was a "historic" achievement. President of the ICAO Council Roberto Kobeh Gonzalez who, articulated that the achievement of the 38th session of the Assembly on climate change would be the "legacy" he leaves behind at the end of his tenure in 2013 said: "The MBM agreement is a historic milestone for air transport and for the role of multilateralism in addressing global climate challenges".[25] It would be stretching one's imagination to believe that a vague resolution to develop an MBM scheme which would only be applicable in 2020 is a "historic" achievement.

---

[24] *Supra*, Preface.

[25] http://www.icao.int/Newsroom/Pages/mbm-agreement-solid-global-plan-endoresements.aspx.

A more sensible and down to earth statement was issued by Flying Clean Alliance Director Shelby White who said:

> ICAO has been talking about dealing with carbon pollution from airplanes for 16 years, but doing nothing. The agency can't just keep playing its old game of promising climate action—next time—and then failing to deliver. Climate change is costing the aviation industry billions of dollars in cancelled flights from extreme weather, and hurting the whole planet.[26]

Historically, ICAO's record in dealing with this subject reeks of the Organization's own insouciance and lack of awareness of the magnitude of the problem. At its 21st Assembly (Montreal, 21st September-15 October 1974) ICAO was both ambivalent and resistant on fuel efficiency standards for new aircraft and in 2004 rejected a global emissions trading system. If a global MBM would have been made applicable in 2012. aviation's contribution to global warming could have been reduced by 31 %. Instead, pushing it all back to 2020 is just plain lethargy and feckless incompetence. To sum up popular comment:

(a) No concrete action was taken at the Montreal assembly. Delegates merely authorized ICAO to develop a global MBM mechanism over the next 3 years. According to an ICAO spokesperson, the details "will be determined over the course of the coming triennium, based on discussions amongst our member states,";
(b) Even if the next ICAO assembly adopts the plan in 2016, it won't take effect until 2020;
(c) Until then, the sector's emissions will continue to rise, as increases in passenger volume offset incremental improvements in fuel efficiency.[27]

Establishing the Balance

The leadership of ICAO (under the new President of the Council) should restore the relevancy and credibility of ICAO by establishing time lines and a work programme for the next 3 years that would ensure ICAO's delivery to the 39th session of the Assembly an MBM scheme that is workable and applicable in 2020. The current approach adopted by the Council (which has been a practice for many decades) of establishing and adopting a work programme for each session of the Council and muddling through its overall responsibility in this instance simply will not work, as was proven in the last triennium. The 3 years work programme should not be couched in ambivalent terms and ambiguous text which does not give either the Council or the Secretariat purpose and direction. Secondly, ICAO should

---

[26] Gut Lavigueur, Airline's Carbon Reduction Plan Spins Out of Control, http://theenergycollective.com/mitchell-beer/287336/airlines-carbon-reduction-plan-spins-out-control.
[27] Ibid.

approach its work in a structured manner by gaining insight and comprehension of what is meant by CBDR and, more importantly SCRC. Thus far, neither ICAO nor any member State of the Organization has defined SCRC of various categories of States in the context of the subject at hand—within the rubric of aviation or air transport. Thirdly, ICAO should ensure that any MBM scheme should not entail a disadvantage to any State while conferring an advantage to another State. In other words, the scheme proposed must be paretian. Such a scheme should also be ethically sound and politically feasible. More importantly, the focus of the scheme must primarily be to reduce emissions rather than to punish emissions.

I have already elaborated on the CBDR principle in an earlier publication[28] which should be read in conjunction with this article. As for SCRC, ICAO's primary task is to place it in context. For instance, what are the special circumstances and respective capabilities of States that have to be taken into consideration? The answer to this question would lie in the fact that the principal duty of States is to meet the needs of the people of the world (through ICAO) for safe, regular, efficient and economical air transport.[29] What are the circumstances involved in achieving this goal and what are States' respective capabilities in ensuring that the implementation of this principle attains fruition? These questions clearly show that any MBM scheme that bases itself on emissions trading will not be isolated from other relevant and critical factors of air transport such as trade-offs for States and their airlines which show SCRC. Although ICAO is not in a position to offer trade-offs ICAO can nonetheless suggest tangible trade-offs. In order to do this ICAO would have to strengthen its Secretariat's expertise and encourage innovation and creativity within its ranks. Professionals who have the requisite qualifications and specialization in environmental economics should be put to work to come up with basic options without first summoning States, international organizations and experts for initial guidance. Although the task should largely be accomplished by consultation with States and other key players, the experts in the ICAO Secretariat should play a larger role than they play at present.

The key driver in this task is distributive justice and ethics based on the Pareto Principle. This principle advocates the view that a project is socially desirable if it makes at least one person better off than in the status quo and makes no person worse off.[30] Paretianism is a welfarist principle that is consistent with the expectations of the SCRC principle which in turn is the bulwark of the mandate facing ICAO.

It is incontrovertible that all of humankind will be worse off in the future if climate change is not addressed both aggressively and diligently. The Fifth

---

[28] See Abeyratne, *supra* note 194, at 22–24.

[29] *Id.* at 1–11.

[30] See Eric A. Posner and David Weighbach, *International Paretianism: A Defence*, The Law School, University of Chicago, July 2012 at 2. See also Gabriel A. Sanchez, In Defence of Incrementalism for International Aviation Emissions Regulation, *Virginia Journal of International Law Digest*, Vol. 53, 2012 at 2.

Assessment of the Inter Government Panel on Climate Change (IPCC) released in 2013 States:

> Warming of the climate system is unequivocal, and since the 1950s many of the observable changes are unprecedented over decades to millennia, the atmosphere and ocean have warmed, the amounts of snow and ice have diminished, sea level has risen and the concentration of gases has increased.[31]

The Report also mentions that human influence has been detected in warming of the atmosphere and ocean, in changes in the global water cycle, in reduction in snow and ice, in global mean sea level rise and in changes in some climate extremes.[32] These findings call for a compelling need for mitigation, which in turn could create a surplus that could be distributed among States in the nature of credits. This would benefit even States that do not experience severe deleterious effects of climate change.

In developing a Paretian model (in close consultation with member States and other key players) ICAO will have to be cautious of the fact that States will try to negotiate the best deal for themselves and maximise their gain from an MBM scheme. Developing States will expect a redistribution of wealth and untrammelled development of their air transport industry and services, the latter of which is important toward meeting the present and future needs of the people of the world for air transport services.

CBDR and SCRC

The common but differentiated responsibilities (CBDR) principle is enshrined in the mandate of ICAO, as prescribed in the Assembly Resolution. Although sovereign equality of States is an established principle of public international law, and one which guides ICAO in its work, sovereign equality does not mean that all ICAO member States are equal in substantive terms. The variance of size, demographies, power and natural wealth in each State make it difficult to speak of sovereign equality of States in substantive terms. In the context of air transport CBDR becomes an essential principle when considering the different exigencies that exist between States in which the air transport industry is highly developed and established and States in which the industry is not as developed. The latter should not be unnecessarily fettered by stringent environmental penalties that would effectively preclude and stultify growth in the sector.

CBDR is based on equity and justice and the inescapable reality that it is essential for ensuring continued growth of developing States:

---

[31] Working Group 1 Contribution to the IPCC Fifth Assessment Report, *Climate Change 2013: The Physical Science Basis-Summary for Policy Makers* IPCC-WG1 AR5, SPM-2, 27 September 2013 at 2.

[32] *Id.* 11.

Recognition of the differentiated responsibilities was at the political heart of the UNCED[33] synthesis because developing States were unwilling to have global environmental problems impede their development. Differentiated responsibilities also reflect equitable norms concerning the use of resources and treatment of nations with varying capabilities (Dernbach 1998).

The first task of ICAO would be to have a clear understanding of CBDR and SCRC of its member States in relation to MBMs by undertaking a comprehensive study. During the triennium 2010–2013 the Counci of ICAO went through consultations with States under an explicit mandate from the 37th session of the Assembly (2010) to:

Explore the feasibility of a long term global aspirational goal for international aviation, through conducting detailed studies assessing the attainability and impacts of any goals proposed in including the impact of growth as well as costs in all States, especially developing States, for the progress of the work to be presented to the 38th session of the assembly. Assessment of long term goals should include information from member States on their experiences working toward the medium term good.[34]

The 37th session of the Assembly reiterated this request elsewhere in Resolution A37-19 stressing the importance of this requirement. The Assembly requested:

The Council, with the support of member States and international organizations to continue to explore the feasibility of a global MBM scheme by undertaking further studies on the technical aspects, environmental benefits, economic impacts and the modalities of such a scheme.[35]

Simply put, while the 37th session of the Assembly required the Council to explore the feasibility and modalities of an MBM scheme, the 38th session in 2013 agreed to develop such a scheme. In other words while the Council took 3 years to explore the feasibility of an MBM scheme, it will take another 3 years to come up with an MBM scheme that the Assembly will finally develop. It will take 6 years in all while the world waits.

The ICAO Council could well be guided by some treaties outside the realm of environmental protection for analogy. In particular, the Law of the Sea Convention (UNCLOS) which, on the subject of preferential treatment for developing States provides that:

Developing States shall, for purposes of prevention, reduction and control of pollution of the maritime environment or minimalization of its efforts, be granted preference by international organizations in (a) the allocation of appropriate funds and technical assistance; and (b) the utilization of their specialized services.[36]

---

[33] United Nations Conference on Environmental Development, also known as the Earth Summit (Rio de Janeiro: 1992).

[34] Assembly Resolution 37–19 paragraph 8.

[35] *Id.* paragraph 18.

[36] United Nations Convention on the Law of the Sea (UNCLOS), 21 *ILM* [26] (1982), Article 203.

By this provision, UNCLOS requires States, directly or through competent international Organizations to promote programmes of scientific, educational, technical and other assistance as well as provide adequate funds. It is also note-worthy that the Agreement Establishing the World Trade Organization[37] in its Preamble distinguishes between developed and developing States as well as least developed States. The Agreement calls for positive measures to ensure that developing States and also least developed States "secure a share in the growth in international trade commensurate with the needs of their economic development". Although, like ICAO, the basic principle of WTO is non discrimination, the WTO Agreement recognizes the need to grant special and differential treatment for developing and least developed States.

Additionally, at the Doha Ministerial Conference[38] some members of WTO proposed, as part of the Ministerial Declaration, the adoption of a framework agreement on special and differential treatment. Under the WTO umbrella, least developed States have been given preferential recognition. For instance, they were granted an extension until 1 July 2013 to provide for an intellectual property regime under the TRIPs Agreement.[39] This decision also calls upon least developed country member States to provide WTO with as much information as possible on their priority needs for technical and financial cooperation with a view to assisting them to take necessary measures to comply with the TRIPs agreement.

To go a step further, the United Nations Convention on Desertification gives preferential treatment to a whole continent—Africa—calling for developed States to give necessary assistance to African States. The Rotterdam Convention on Prior Informed Consent for Certain Hazardous Chemicals and Pesticides in International Trade[40] and the Stockholm Convention on Persistent Organic Pollutants[41] are also good examples. The former requires States Parties to the Convention to take into account the particular needs of developing States and States with economies in transition, cooperate in promoting technical assistance for the development of infrastructure and capacity necessary to implement the provisions of the Convention.

The process before the ICAO Council for the 2014–2016 triennium has incontrovertibly to be approached in stages. The first step is to recognize that this time around, it is the Assembly that will develop an MBM scheme based on input provided by the Council. Usually the Assembly directs the Council to develop such a scheme and endorses it at its session, if the attending member States find it

---

[37] The World Trade Organization (WTO) is the only global international organization dealing with the rules of trade between nations. At its heart are the WTO agreements, negotiated and signed by the bulk of the world's trading nations and ratified in their parliaments. The goal is to help producers of goods and services, exporters, and importers conduct their business.

[38] Doha Ministerial Conference, 9–13 November 2001.

[39] Decision of the Council of TRIPs, November 2005. TRIPs stand for Trade Related Intellectual Property.

[40] 38 ILM 1 (1999).

[41] UN Doc UNEP/POPS/CONF/4, 40 ILM 532 (2001).

acceptable. By implication therefore, the 39th session of the Assembly will need much more time to fine tune and finally develop the scheme than it devoted to discuss the subject at its 38th session. The Council, and indeed the Secretariat of ICAO should start with this premise, which would essentially lead to detailed studies on critical issues involved including but not limited to CBDR and SCRC. This obviously requires astringent work programme for 3 years to be agreed by the Council early in 2014.

Next, the Council will have to well inform itself of SCRC in order to develop a framework on MBMs that would be acceptable to the Assembly. Many States recorded their reservations to the clause in the Resolution which required that consideration be given to CBDR and SCRC[42] Therefore, it goes without saying that the Council will have to conduct diligent consultations with member States and international Organizations (which means the Secretariat will have to do the groundwork). Responsibility should devolve upon the Secretary General to ensure that the background work is done with competence, knowledge and diligence. Such a task would involve not only knowledge but creativity and insight. Insight is critical which is much more valuable than perceived knowledge. Trusting in procedure rather than people has been a general characteristic of ICAO. More damagingly, giving credibility to positions and grades over actual knowledge and creativity has damaged ICAO's progress. In professional terms this is called "organizational repression" (See Klein 2013). As Einstein said: "The real obstacle to knowledge is not ignorance by the illusion of knowledge". ICAO's organizational performance should turn positive with insight. For this to be achieved, fewer insights should get blocked, and creativity should be encouraged. One commentator says:

> One way to counter an Organization's tendency to edit things to death is to set up an alternate reporting route so that knowledge workers can publish opinion pieces that don't have to go through routine editing. This alternate publishing method would escape the filters.[43]

ICAO could well do with this approach in general as well as in specific terms with regard to the development of an MBM scheme. Blocking insight through bureaucratic filtering leads to the greater damage of insights not being actioned. This retroactive approach could easily undermine the development of an MBM scheme. The result would be that the Organization would lack the willpower to make changes. In ICAO every bit of writing has to go through persons euphemistically called a "chief" or "Director" as the case may be, who often arrogate to themselves an omniscient role over and above their supervisory and managerial role. In such instances Einstein's "illusion of knowledge" comes into play as these persons may not have the requisite qualifications, knowledge or experience in the

---

[42] Guiding Principle (p) to Resolution A38-18. The States which recorded their reservations are Australia, Canada, Japan, Lithuania (on behalf of 28 member States of the European Unon and 14 other member States of the European Civil Aviation Conference, New Zealand, The Republic of Korea and the United states.

[43] *Id.* 212.

specialized aviation subjects they supervise Although this practice may be usual, however repulsive and unethical, in a highly politicized system of appointment to posts as in ICAO, in the context of the task at hand with regard to the MBM scheme, this mindset will have to go if results are to be shown to the 39th session of the Assembly.

One of the considerations that might be of assistance to ICAO is the convincing argument put forward by the welfarists—mostly developing States. They advocate the per capita approach over the status quo approach on the basis that wealthy nations should not be given an entitlement or "blank cheque" to their existing rights. This argument based on fairness is plausible to the extent that a welfarist approach would result in maximizing the pie and distributing it equally. Developing States tend to have larger populations which would do well with the welfare or per capita principle. In this regard ICAO would have to at least consider in some depth as to how it could involve and make use of its much vaunted and sometimes effective Technical Cooperation Programme[44] into the equation which would provide technical assistance to the least developed and developing States[45] as part of the MBM Scheme.

A Report released in late 2013 by Oxford University, called the *Oxford Martin Report*) on governance for the future recognized that climate change and its effects in the long term should be immediately addressed. Encouragingly, ICAO is well on its way in this regard. The Oxford report suggests that in the long term States should create a C20-C30-C40 Coalition to counteract climate change; a new coalition made up of G20 States, 30 companies, and 40 cities.[46] The coalition could accelerate action on climate change, with measurable targets *inter alia* for initiatives that include tracking emissions.[47] This might be one of the first steps ICAO might wish to consider taking.

---

[44] In March 2011, at its 192nd Session, the Council of the International Civil Aviation Organization, requested the Secretary General to review internally the issue of technical assistance and to formulate a policy therein to be discussed during a future Council Session. In May 2012, the Finance Committee and Technical Cooperation Committee of the Council considered the Organization's proposed new technical assistance policy, whereby ICAO commits to render technical assistance to its member States which will enhance their ability to achieve measurable and sustainable results in their implementation of and compliance with ICAO Standards and Recommended Practices. Such assistance would enable capacity building in air navigation and air transport activities and include but not be limited to the conduct of and assistance pertaining to training courses, seminars, and the provision of expert opinion.

[45] The Technical Cooperation Programme (TCP) of ICAO which is executed by the Technical Cooperation Bureau (TCB) that was established in 1952, has maintained a sustained record of technical assistance provided to States for over 60 years. TCP is the major operational tool for reinforcing the Organization's technical cooperation mission objectives, including enhancing the capacity of developing States to implement ICAO Standards and Recommended Practices (SARPs). Its continuing importance has been reaffirmed by the Assembly in several resolutions.

[46] *Now For The Long Term, Oxford Martin Commission for Future Generations*, http://oneworld.org/2013/10/15/report-calls-for-action-on-climate-poverty-governance-and-disease, at 57.

[47] Ibid.

References

Gore AL (2006) An inconvenient truth. Rodale, New York, p 25

Monbiot G (2006) Heat-how to stop the planet from burning. Doubleday, Ontario, p 8

Marsa L (2013) Fevered, why a hot planet will hurt our health—and how we can save ourselves. Rodale, Emmaus, p 19

Dernbach J (1998) Sustainable development as a framework for national governance. 49 Case W Res L Rev 1:26

Klein G (2013) Seeing what others don't—the remarkable ways we gain insights. Public Affairs, New York, pp 162–169

Chapter 5
Required Initial Strategy

The first step for ICAO in this process would be to carefully study the consequences of a global market based measure (MBM) would bring for both developed and developing States, through carefully selected key stakeholders (the Oxford Study's recommendation might be a good start) with the expertise available at the Secretariat. In that Report, Pascal Lamy (former head of the World Trade Organization) who headed the Commission that produced the document said:

> The ability to address today's global challenges is undermined by the absence of a collective vision for society. We urge leaders to establish shared global values to protect the prospects for future generations.[1]

Professor Ian Golding, Deputy Head of the Commission said:

> Failure to address long-term issues exposes current generations to unacceptable instability and risk; it threatens our ability to build a sustainable, inclusive and resilient future for all.[2]

The key concept here is a collective vision for society and not another polarized debate between developed and developing nations on how a market based measure might stultify the growth of developing States. To narrow the concept further, there must be a collective vision for the development of aviation in a fair and equitable manner. In other words, ICAO must devise a *global air transport environmental policy* first that would receive approbation of the 36 members of the Council that represents all 191 member States of ICAO and which would serve States equitably based on the challenges that free market economic policies might bring. The first step in moving toward a global air transport environment policy is to build shared global values. The common platform of understanding that all States should build is one of a shared vision for global civilization through development based on the potential of growth of each country balanced by a

---

[1] http://www.oxfordmartin.ox.ac.uk/commission.
[2] Ibid.

© The Author(s) 2014
R. Abeyratne, *Aviation and Climate Change*, SpringerBriefs in Law,
DOI: 10.1007/978-3-319-08443-5_5

degree of compromise that would obviate "tunnel vision" toward growth at all cost. In other words, opportunism, should be eschewed and instead preference for common growth should be the priority.

In the above context, any work toward a global market based measure would fail, and indeed be baseless if an in-depth study of global trends over the next 20 years is not undertaken through clusters of States that form separate groups along the lines suggested by the *Oxford Martin Report*. Again to quote Pascal Lamy:

> Global governance and cooperation will remain an alien concept as long as there is no feeling of global belonging among citizens. Too many States feel that current global models and methods are embedded in a historical, "Western" framework. In today's interconnected world, we need a common platform for dialogue that speaks to all cultures and States and seeks to advance common understanding and build a better world for future generations.[3]

The question is, how could this lofty and eminently sensible approach be put into practice? Through what mechanism? This would be through an initial identification of shared global values.

Shared Global Values

Shared global values must essentially be based on all States accepting reality as to where the world is headed in terms of growth and how global growth would impact air transport. ICAO's partnership with key stakeholders would be critical in this regard and the Organization's Air Transport Bureau should be the main driver in studying global trends. Such a study should look into both the developed world and the developing world, keeping in mind the two fundamental principles of CBDR and SCRC.

The first shared global value would start with the ultimate constitutional instrument of aviation—the Chicago Convention[4]—and that value is fair and equal opportunity in providing air transport. States must have fair and equal opportunity given to their carriers to provide air transport and this right cannot be eroded by unfair charges that put them at a disadvantage over other carriers of other States. The CBDR approach, which ascribes some flexibility in responsibility for the environment with regard to disadvantaged States could be viewed in the light of an extension, conceptually towards the *Special but Differentiated Treatment* (SDT) approach of the World Trade Organization.[5] Although trade is not the only means of achieving development, trade is one of the foremost driver of development in

---

[3] Oxford Martin Report, *supra*, note 1 at 63.

[4] *Supra*, note 1.

[5] *Supra*, note 136.

the air transport field as a yardstick of a country's development. Therefore work in developing a global market based measure should take into account the fact that an MBM as a trading tool should not hamper the development of States that are in the process of development. Therefore an SDT approach should not be an obstacle to international or national strategies in development.

The second shared goal must be that States should be initially requested to define their own interests in the CBDR, SCRC and SDT interests and that developed States should not be allowed to prescribe, recommend or demand what is good for the developing States. ICAO would tread a delicate balance in this instance and it would take many discussions at a Council Study Group to arrive at that balance. An SDT approach so developed must be able to achieve a total integration of all 191 member States of ICAO. It must also be cost efficient and equitable so that no country loses while others gain.

The third shared goal would be to reach a fair extrapolation of what States would need special consideration in developing a global MBM. This could be controversial and a study should endeavour to avoid naming States and instead identify interests of types of States or groups of States. These goals would provide the initial basis for a shared global vision to set the tone for a global MBM.

Global Market Trends

Inherent to a global vision is the acceptance of the realities of market economics. In March 2010, Larry Elliott, writing to the Guardian said of the decade 2010–2020:

> Get ready for the austerity decade. Forget all thoughts that the economic storm of the past 30 months is about to blow over. We've had what Mervyn King once called the NICE period of non-inflationary constant expansion but now we face a long DRAG—deficit reduction, anemic growth. The lessons of economic history, the current configuration of the economy, and inescapable long-term challenges that have to be faced provide the same message: it's payback time.[6]

Perhaps it is, and if there were to be anemic growth in the years ahead, indubitably the downturn would affect air transport adversely. The problem with air transport is that, while on the one hand it is a product, on the other hand regulations pertaining to this product may constrain its availability to the consumer by depriving him of the various choices of air travel he might have under a liberalized system. In other words, State policy and the protection of national interests take precedence over the interest of the user of air transport. The aviation industry offers only one product to the ultimate consumer and that is the air transport product. One might well ask why this product is precluded from attracting untrammeled foreign direct investment (FDI) like other products such as those in

---

[6] http://www.guardian.co.uk/business/2010/mar/01/drag-deficit-reduction-anaemic-growth.

the agriculture, textile manufacture and energy industries. In this context, the next chapter will discuss the course air transport would have to take to cope with the economic trends facing us in order to keep offering services in response to continuing demand.

One consideration would be to look at the shared vision together with the growth and development trends in the world with a view to evaluating the possibility of tying the criteria of a global MBM to CBDR, SCRC and SDT. A study of the global growth charts of countries could enable ICAO to develop a living MBM mechanism that could be revisited and adjusted periodically. At the time of writing the world was in convergence from east to west and a shared global vision for aviation and climate change was a distinct possibility. Free market economics was considered the only viable tool for attaining prosperity. A multilateral and global MBM concept and a shared vision to effect accords well with the theory of *One World*. The yardstick of growth and development as a common benchmark is becoming relevant as each every passes. Former British Prime Minister Tony Blair has said:

> Under the momentum of globalization the world is opening up and countries and cultures are coming closer...we live in a completely new and different world today. There is a completely different complexion to the way politics works today.[7]

A Statement by another former British Prime Minister Gordon Brown is consistent with Blair's view where Brown opines that the world's economies are intrinsically and integrally connected and that global economic problems should be addressed with a view to seeking global solutions and global institutions (Brown 2010).

Kishore Mahbubani observes:

> Any theory of one world should begin with the environmental pillar as there is now a global awareness the 7 billion occupants (the number will rise to 9 billion by 2050) of planet Earth are not doing a good job of managing the only planet in the universe that we know to be capable of hosting human life. We do not have a second option, no planet to migrate to if we fail to preserve this one's environment (Mahbubani 2013).

There is, as to be expected, an opposing view—that one has to approach this absolute belief in multilateralism with some caution and reservation. Fareed Zakaria is of the view:

> The rise of the Rest, while real, is a long process. And it is one that ensures America a vital, though different role. As China, India, Brazil, Russia, South Africa and a host of smaller countries all do well in the years ahead, new points of tension will emerge among them. Many of these rising countries have historical animosities, border disputes and contemporary quarrels with one another, in most cases, nationalism will grow along with economic and geopolitical stature (Zakaria 2012).

---

[7] Tony Blair, As the World Becomes Smaller, the Need to Understand Each Other's Faith Grows, *The Independent*, June 4 2008.

This disconcerting fact certainly puts a damper in the concept of a global shared vision and therefore some caution must be exercised in carefully considering the politico-economic trends that affects particularly the BRICs States. Ruchir Sharma is of the view that China's growth will fall to 5–6 % in the next few years as its development rate is too quick and cannot be sustained and other major players including Brazil, Russia and India "face their own daunting challenges and inflated expectations" (Sharma 2012). Sharma says:

> The notion of wide ranging convergence between the developing and developed world is a myth. Of the roughly 180 countries in the world tracked by the International Monetary Fund, only 35 are developed. The markets of the rest are emerging, and most of them have been emerging for many decades and will continue to do so for many more.[8]

Sharma hastens to add that this is not a negative read on emerging markets but a historical fact. Although in the beginning of the 21st Century emerging markets were hyped as exotic and influential economic factors, countries such as Thailand and Malaysia from which much was expected had proved to be disappointing. Burma, the Philippines and Sri Lanka were also considered emerging markets in the 1960s only to falter and stagnate. The promising economic uprising of Taiwan (in 1991); India (in 1992); Russia (in 1995) and South Korea (in 1993) was thwarted by economic crises that affected the West between 1994 and 2002. Sharma says that the second resurgence started in 2003 and the third resurgence is yet to come though its results could be uneven.[9]

The two conflicting views: one which on the one hand expresses confidence on convergence and another on the other hand expresses concern over the economic unpredictability of breakout nations, have to be viewed in the context of the G20 countries which include large economies of the European Union, The United States, Canada, Australia, New Zealand, South Korea and the BRICs nations which account for between 85–90 % of the global income, spread across approximately two thirds of the global population. The G20 Group came into being with the global realization that, although at that time the existing G7/8 countries were economically and politically influential, emerging economies had to be part of the overall equation particularly in the aftermath of the 2008–2009 economic crisis. Here we could go back to the *Oxford Martin Report*[10] in the context of the consultative relevance of the G20 Group in formulating a shared vision leading to a global MBM.

The relevance of growth as a consideration in the development of a global MBM can be analogically applied to some compelling questions posed by Nobel laureate Michael Spence:

---

[8] Ruchir Sharma, Broken BRICs: Why the Rest Stopped Rising, *Foreign Affairs*, November/December 2012 Issue at 32.

[9] Ibid.

[10] *Supra*, note 1.

Will the high speed growth in the developing world continue? On what does that continuation depend? Are there economic and environmental headwinds that will slow the growth and reduce opportunities? Will the countries that have thus far not grown much—or when they have, only fitfully—achieve a pattern of steadier and higher growth, or with the world divide into a majority that is relatively rich and minority that remains relatively poor? (Spence 2011).

Spence also asks the question as to whether such growth would be sustainable in terms of energy availability and cost and in terms of air quality, climate change and water availability, which are valuable considerations for a global MBM.

The bottom line in the shared vision of a global MBM would lie in a difference in approach—in not distinguishing between equality of outcome and equality of opportunity. Thus far, the debate on MBMs has been that restrictions on aviation emissions and penalties connected therewith would result in unequal opportunities for developing countries that have emerging markets to grow and develop, which would result in unequal outcomes. These countries ask the question as to why they have to bite the bullet now while developed countries have had years of untrammelled rides in their development without such penalties being imposed on them. The economist Milton Friedman argued that a search for equality would inevitably focus more on the equality of outcome rather than the equality of opportunity. Pankaj Ghemawat argues:

> The distinction between equalization of outcomes and of opportunities in indeed important. But the trade off that Friedman highlights is just a possibility that is particularly likely to apply if the equalization of outcomes is pushed too far (Ghemawat 2011).

This is indeed correct and those who develop a global MBM should be cautious as to not push either of the factors—equality of outcome and equality of opportunity too far. Ghemawat attributed fears of exploitation as a distinct obstacle to creating value and explains that integration and regulation almost always meet the roadblock of shifts in how benefits are shared. He claims that it is a toss-up between claiming value and creating value and that if a distinction is not made between these two, any attempt at integration would be futile.[11]

As stated earlier, The Oxford Martin Report's, recommendation of involving country groups such as the G20 in the participatory process could result in real value creation in the pursuit of real a shared global; view of an MBM and could well lie in a set of horizontal networks among national government officials, technical experts in environmental economics and law. ICAO is a club States and therefore dogmatically involves State in all its discussions, perhaps rightly so but could do well to recognize the basic truth about current reality—that while the State is by no means disappearing, it is disaggregating into component institutions which are increasingly interacting with key stakeholders and counterparts across borders (Slaughter 2004).

---

[11] Id. 261.

References

Brown G (2010) Beyond the crash: overcoming crisis globalization. Simon & Schuster, New York, p 21

Ghemawat P (2011) World 3.0: global prosperity and how to achieve it. Harvard Business Review Press, Boston, p 185

Mahbubani K (2013) The great convergence: Asia the west and the logic of the world. Public Affairs, New York, p 55

Sharma R (2012) Breakout nations: in pursuit of the next economic miracles. WW Norton & Company, New York (book jacket)

Slaughter A-M (2004) A new world order. Princeton University Press, Princeton, pp 18–19

Spence M (2011) The next convergence: the future of economic growth in a multispeed world. Farrar, Straus and Giroux, New York, p 129

Zakaria F (2012) The post American world, release 2.0. WW Norton & Company, New York, p 257

Chapter 6
Follow Up Strategy

Once a shared view is established and a trend analysis through appropriate studies (conducted by the ICAO Secretariat) are carried out on the growth trends of the world, the next step would be to consider the parameters of international law which ICAO is obligated to come within if a global market based measure were to be introduced under the aegis of ICAO. Firstly, ICAO is a specialized agency of the United Nations.[1] Under the United Nations Charter, ICAO has responsibilities under its constituent instrument—the Chicago Convention. Therefore ICAO has to recognize and follow the first principle of the Chicago Convention which, in Article 1 provides that Contracting States (to the Chicago Convention) recognize that every State (including those that have not signed or otherwise ratified the Chicago Convention) has complete and exclusive sovereignty over the airspace above its territory which is defined as the land areas and territorial waters adjacent thereto under the sovereignty, suzerainty, protection or mandate of such State.

---

[1] Article 57 of the Charter of the United Nations provides that the various specialized agencies, established by intergovernmental agreement and having wide international responsibilities, as defined in their basic instruments, in economic, social, cultural, educational, health, and related fields, shall be brought into relationship with the United Nations in accordance with the provisions of Article 63. Such agencies thus brought into relationship with the United Nations are referred to as specialized agencies. Article 63 stipulates that The Economic and Social Council may enter into agreements with any of the agencies referred to in Article 57, defining the terms on which the agency concerned shall be brought into relationship with the United Nations. Such agreements shall be subject to approval by the General Assembly. It may co-ordinate the activities of the specialized agencies through consultation with and recommendations to such agencies and through recommendations to the General Assembly and to the Members of the United Nations.

© The Author(s) 2014
R. Abeyratne, *Aviation and Climate Change*, SpringerBriefs in Law,
DOI: 10.1007/978-3-319-08443-5_6

Therefore a global MBM must have a territorial applicability and must not admit of extra territoriality.[2]

Extra territorial jurisdiction is where the authority of a State to legislate reaches out beyond its territorial boundaries with a trading scheme which may run the risk of being accused of extra territorial application of that scheme. As a legal concept, the issue of emissions trading brings to bear the issue as to whether a single State or a group of States could unilaterally impose a trading scheme on air carriers requiring the acquisition by such carriers of carbon credits pertaining to emissions over territories other than the territories of the imposing State or States. The question that naturally arises is whether such a measure would be an extra territorial application of laws.

Extra territorial jurisdiction is exercised when a State (or in this case a community of States) seeks to apply its laws outside its territory in such a manner as may cause conflicts with other States.[3] It can be justified by the invocation of the effects doctrine or the "effects theory" which goes beyond the principles of sovereignty. This theory relates to a situation where a State assumes jurisdiction beyond its territorial limits on the ground that the behaviour of a party is adversely affecting the interests of that State by producing "effects" within its territory. It does not matter whether all the conduct and practices take place in another State or whether part of the conduct is within the State adopting the legislation. In the latter instance, the conduct of the party would come under the "objective territorial principle" where part of the offence takes place within the jurisdiction. In the case of aircraft engine emissions, the applicable principles would come under both headings as trans-boundary pollution of the environment by an aircraft which flies into Europe may involve the emissions of gases in one State that could cross boundaries and affect Europe.

With regard to territorial waters, The United Nations Convention on the Law of the Sea (UNCLOS)[4] which was signed by the Parties on December 10, 1982 and entered into force on November 16, 1994 after receiving 60 ratifications or accessions, divides the seas into zones over which States have varying degrees of

---

[2] In 2012, ICAO undertook a study calculated to result in a framework of market based measures that would respond globally to the adverse effects of aircraft engine emissions. This was in direct response to a call by 26 member States of the ICAO Council including China, Russia, India and the United States which, in late 2011 had protested against the emissions trading scheme (EU ETS) of the European Union applicable to air transport. ICAO has been considering as an option for a global MBM an ETS scheme much along the lines of the EU ETS but on a global level that would not entail issues of extra territoriality and infringements of sovereignty as claimed by the many detractors of the EU ETS.

[3] There is a general common law presumption against the extra territorial application of legislation. See the House of Lords decision in *Holmes* versus *Bangladesh Biman Corporation* [1989] AC 1112 at 1126;

87 ILR 365 at 369. Also, *Air India* versus *Wiggins* [1980] 1WLR 815 t 819; 77 ILR 276 at 27.

[4] Law of the Sea, Official Text of the United Nations Convention on the Law of the Sea with Indexes and Annex, Final Act of the Third United Nations Conference on the Law of the Sea, United Nations: 1983.

rights and controls. The territorial sea, which is exclusively controlled by the State, is the first zone which extends 12 nautical miles from the coast or coastal baselines. The territorial sea is open to all vessels to enjoy the right of innocent passage. Beyond the territorial zone comes the contiguous zone of another 12 nautical miles followed by the exclusive economic zone of 200 nautical miles from the coastal baseline. In Article 76 titled "Definition of the Continental Shelf" UNCLOS provides that a States Party may extend its continental margin beyond the 200 nautical mile Exclusive Economic Zone (EEZ) if certain criteria are fulfilled. Since the Chicago Convention only refers to "territorial waters", one of ICAO's preeminent considerations would be whether, in the development of a global MBM, its application, based on a territorial denomination would apply within a State's sovereign control and application, to the airspace above its land territory, extended merely to 12 nautical miles surrounding the State or to other zones identified by UNCLOS.

Another consideration for ICAO in developing a framework for a global MBM would be Article 12 of the Chicago Convention which provides:

> Each contracting State undertakes to adopt measures to insure that every aircraft flying over or manoeuvring within its territory and that every aircraft carrying its nationality mark, wherever such aircraft may be, shall comply with the rules and regulations relating to the flight and manoeuvre of aircraft there in force. Each contracting State undertakes to keep its own regulations in these respects uniform, to the greatest possible extent, with those established from time to time under this Convention. Over the high seas, the rules in force shall be those established under this Convention. Each contracting State undertakes to insure the prosecution of all persons violating the regulations applicable.

Article 12 has significant nuances which ICAO will be bound by in the context of a global MBM. The first is that the provision refers *inter alia* to "rules" related to flight which could include rules that may be related to aircraft emissions over the high seas. Here, ICAO would be confronted with the question as to how a global MBM might affect flight over the high seas. Would there be a formula for aircraft flying over the high seas to compensate for the pollution they create over the high seas, beyond the territorial limits of any State? If so, how would such compensation be collected? and who would administer such a collection? would the collection be based on a mechanism similar to the joint financing mechanism across the Atlantic which is administered by ICAO[5]?

---

[5] The ICAO Assembly, at its First Session (Montreal 6–27 May 1947) adopted Resolution A1-65 (Joint Support Policy) which resolved that financial and technical aid through ICAO for furthering the provision of air navigation facilities and services adequate for the safe, regular, efficient and economical operation of international air services will be rendered, under the terms of Chapter XV of the Chicago Convention, in accordance with the basic principles and general policy laid down in Annex 1 to Resolution A1-65. The ensuing Joint Financing Agreement of 1948 has since been replaced by the Agreements of 1956 which was amended by the Montreal Protocol of 1982. This agreement requires Iceland and Denmark to operate and maintain air navigation services without interruption and provides for Iceland to be reimbursed by the Contracting States for ninety five per cent of the costs incurred.

Another consideration would be the overall relevance of the "polluter pays" principle within the umbrella of a global MBM and to what extent the developers of such an instrument would consider the principle applicable, particularly in the context of territoriality which, as already discussed, binds ICAO. Here, early developments and case law become relevant.

The United Nations Conference on Sustainable Development (UNCSD, or Rio +10) took place in Brazil on 20–22 June 2012 to mark the 20th anniversary of the 1992 UNCED, in Rio de Janeiro, and the 10th anniversary of the 2002 World Summit on Sustainable Development (WSSD) in Johannesburg. At best, ICAO got a few minutes to say a few words at this conference. At Rio +20 a document called "Outcome Document" was adopted which stated *inter alia* that participant States recall the Stockholm Declaration of the United Nations Conference on the Human Environment adopted at Stockholm on 16 June 1972. The States reaffirmed all the principles of the Rio Declaration on Environment and Development, including, inter alia, the principle of common but differentiated responsibilities, as set out in principle 7 of the Rio Declaration. They further reaffirmed their commitment to fully implement the Rio Declaration on Environment and Development, Agenda 21, the Programme for the Further Implementation of Agenda 21, the Plan of Implementation of the World Summit on Sustainable Development (Johannesburg Plan of Implementation) and the Johannesburg Declaration on Sustainable Development of the World Summit on Sustainable Development.

Rio +10 also reaffirmed the key role of all levels of government and legislative bodies in promoting sustainable development. The Conference further acknowledged efforts and progress made at the local and sub national levels, and recognized the important role that such authorities and communities can play in implementing sustainable development, including by engaging citizens and stakeholders and providing them with relevant information, as appropriate, on the three dimensions of sustainable development. States further acknowledged the importance of involving all relevant decision makers in the planning and implementation of sustainable development policies. They underscored that broad public participation and access to information and judicial and administrative proceedings are essential to the promotion of sustainable development. Sustainable development requires the meaningful involvement and active participation of regional, national and sub national legislatures and judiciaries, and all major groups: women, children and youth, indigenous peoples, non-governmental organizations, local authorities, workers and trade unions, business and industry, the scientific and technological community, and farmers, as well as other stakeholders, including local communities, volunteer groups and foundations, migrants and families as well as older persons and persons with disabilities. In this regard, States agreed to work more closely with the major groups and other stakeholders and encourage their active participation, as appropriate, in processes that contribute to decision-making, planning and implementation of policies and programmes for sustainable development at all levels.

States also acknowledged the role of civil society and the importance of enabling all members of civil society to be actively engaged in sustainable development. They recognized that improved participation of civil society depends upon, *inter alia*, strengthening access to information and building civil society capacity and an enabling environment. Another reckonable fact is that information and communications technology is facilitating the flow of information between governments and the public. In this regard, it is essential to work towards improved access to information and communications technology, especially broadband networks and services, and bridge the digital divide, recognizing the contribution of international cooperation in this regard.

One of the areas in which ICAO has retrogressed is its sole reliance on States as participants. Although ICAO, as a club of States is compelled to involve States, it should enhance its outreach as recognized by Rio +10 to other bodies, communities and societies that would meaningfully contribute to an acceptable global framework leading to an MBM. In this context, and from the perspective of the preceding discussion in this article, ICAO has to follow the principles as enunciated by Rio +10: be consistent with international law; respect each country's national sovereignty over their natural resources taking into account its national circumstances, objectives, responsibilities, priorities and policy space with regard to the three dimensions of sustainable development; be supported by an enabling environment and well-functioning institutions at all levels with a leading role for governments and with the participation of all relevant stakeholders, including civil society; promote sustained and inclusive economic growth, foster innovation and provide opportunities, benefits and empowerment for all and respect of all human rights; take into account the needs of developing countries, particularly those in special situations; and strengthen international cooperation, including the provision of financial resources, capacity-building and technology transfer to developing countries; and effectively avoid unwarranted conditionalities on official development assistance (ODA) and finance.

A significant and indeed relevant recommendation emanating from Rio +10, although only of analogical relevance to ICAO as a general principle, is that any global involvement in sustainable development should not constitute a means of arbitrary or unjustifiable discrimination or a disguised restriction on international trade. It must ensure that environmental measures addressing transboundary or global environmental problems, as far as possible, are based on an international consensus. Such an exercise must also contribute to closing technology gaps between developed and developing countries and reduce the technological dependence of developing countries using all appropriate measures.

Finally, ICAO should be guided by the seminal fact underscored by Rio +10—that that the global nature of climate change calls for the widest possible cooperation by all countries and their participation in an effective and appropriate international response, with a view to accelerating the reduction of global greenhouse gas emissions. In this context of seminal importance is the United Nations Framework Convention on Climate Change which calls for parties to protect the climate system for the benefit of present and future generations of humankind on the basis of equity and in accordance with their common but differentiated responsibilities and respective capabilities. Rio +10 was gravely concerned by the significant gap between the aggregate effect of mitigation pledges by parties in terms of global annual emissions of greenhouse gases by 2020 and aggregate emission pathways consistent with having a likely chance of holding the increase in global average temperature below 2 °C, or 1.5 °C above pre-industrial levels. In this context, of primary importance is the mobilizing of funding from a variety of sources, public and private, bilateral and multilateral, including innovative sources of finance, to support nationally appropriate mitigation actions, adaptation measures, technology development and transfer and capacity-building in developing countries.

Given this context, the economic approach to climate change seems to be based, as Amy Larkin, author of *Environmental Debt* (Larkin 2013) says, on three basic principles: pollution is largely free to the polluter; all business decisions regarding and affecting environmental change is for the short term; and governments subsidize business with no concern for environmental impact. If these three principles were to be meaningfully incorporated into an ICAO recommended regime for a global MBM, there has to be a change of the status quo (which is now based on short term aspirations of various States that are polarized on the issue of rights and duties) that transcends narrow considerations and moves toward a regulatory regime change. Larkin suggests that the three misconceptions cited above should change to: pollution can no longer be free and can no longer be subsidized; the long view must guide all decision making and accounting; and governments play a vital role in catalyzing clean technology.

After ICAO imbues States (with their cooperation and input) with a sound understanding of the co-relation between aviation, climate change and economic trends and comes to a thorough understanding of the parameters of international law that are applicable, the Organization would do well to evaluate and determine the sphere of influence that it would wield on its member States of pushing its framework for a global MBM. To do this ICAO has to start with its own "Strategic" Objective on environmental protection which requires ICAO to minimize the adverse environmental effects of civil aviation activities. This Strategic Objective fosters ICAO's leadership in all aviation-related environmental activities and is consistent with the ICAO and UN system environmental protection policies and practices. The word "leadership" is specifically mentioned in the text of the Strategic Objective. The question is, does ICAO show leadership in the environmental field? Why did it not come up with a "leadership" formula at the 38th Session of the Assembly in 2013 after 3 years of pondering over the subject from the 37th Assembly which took place in 2010?

The problem seems to in the fact that ICAO is adept at one thing: signing joint statements. Take for instance the joint statement on Sustainable Approach to Emissions Reductions, signed between ICAO and the Air Transport Action Group (IATA) at ICAO Headquarters, Montréal, on 13 May 2013. There are several measures that both organizations pledge to take:

(a) Promoting efficiency best practices deriving from technological and operational innovation and infrastructure modernization;

(b) Supporting the deployment of the revised ICAO Global Air Navigation Plan and Aviation System Block Upgrade strategy to enhance the efficiency and harmonization of global air traffic management;

(c) Encouraging further research, development and commercialization of sustainable biofuels for aviation, as well as their widespread use by the airline industry;

(d) Encouraging further work toward a global solution for market-based measures applicable to international civil aviation activity;

(e) Encouraging industry to support the development and implementation of States' Action Plans on aviation CO2 emissions; and

(f) Continuing to improve our scientific understanding of aviation's impacts on the global climate. Joint Statement to cooperate on the promotion of sustainable approaches to global aviation emissions reduction

The fundamental flaw is typical—All the lofty measures are driven by words such as "supporting"; "encouraging"; and "continuing to improve". How does ICAO "encourage"—for instance further work "work toward a global solution for market-based measures applicable to international civil aviation activity"? Would it be by constantly writing the typical ICAO "State Letter" its member States? Is this "leadership" that ICAO so liberally claims in all its activities.

Reference

Larkin A (2013) Environmental debt: the hidden cost s of a changing global economy. Palgrave Macmillan, New York, pp 7–8

Chapter 7
ICAO's Work in Developing a Global MBM

In 2013, presumably after the 38th Session of the ICAO Assembly had concluded in October 2013, ICAO officially released its *Report of the Assessment of Market Based Measures*[1] which was based on the input of MBM experts nominated and appointed by States to help ICAO who had shared their expertise and knowledge with the Organization. This Report revealed that while an MBM scheme would provide the environmental benefit of offsetting 464 Mega tonnes of CO_2 in 2036, international aviation traffic under an MBM scheme would grow 107 % from 2020 to 2036. However, without the scheme the traffic level would have grown 110 %. This would mean that an MBM scheme would curtail air traffic by 3 % over that period of timer. For the same period profits for the international aviation sector in 2036 would be US$33.3 billion under the scenario with an MBM scheme which would be $0.4 billion lower than the profit level without the scheme. The cost an MBM scheme would entail in 2036 would be approximately $10 per seat for a flight of 10,000–20,000 km and $1.5 per seat on an flight of 900–1,900 km. These figures meant that an MBM scheme could stabilize CO_2 emissions aircraft at a relatively low cost.[2]

The Report claims that the quantitative and qualitative assessments carried out took into consideration the interests of the developing countries based on the need to factor in SCRC of those States. As discussed in the first Chapter of this book, which alluded to Assembly Resolution A37-19 (Consolidated statement of continuing ICAO policies and practices related to environmental protection—climate change) adopted at the 37th ICAO Assembly in 2010 which requested that ICAO continue to explore the feasibility of a global MBM scheme.

Accordingly, ICAO, with the assistance and input of experts nominated by States had analysed three options for a global MBM: global mandatory offsetting; global mandatory offsetting with revenue; and global emissions trading. The

---

[1] ICAO Doc 10018, First Edition 2013.
[2] Id. (VII)–(VIII).

© The Author(s) 2014
R. Abeyratne, *Aviation and Climate Change*, SpringerBriefs in Law,
DOI: 10.1007/978-3-319-08443-5_7

Report concluded that the results of the qualitative and quantitative analyses of the three options (global mandatory offsetting, global mandatory offsetting with revenue, and global emissions trading) showed that all three options are technically feasible and have the capacity to contribute to achieving ICAO's environmental goals. It also said that global mandatory offsetting could be less complex than global mandatory offsetting complemented by a revenue generation mechanism and global emissions trading.

The Report claimed that global mandatory offsetting complemented by a revenue generation mechanism could be more complex than global mandatory offsetting, due to the need to establish revenue generation and disbursement mechanisms. It would also be necessary to decide on how revenue will be used. The economic impact on participants is more significant than global mandatory offsetting. However, raising revenue creates a revenue stream that could be used to mitigate the environmental impacts of aircraft engine emissions, including mitigation and adaptation, as well as assistance to and support for developing States, as per the guiding principle n) in Resolution A37-19, Annex. Furthermore the Report concluded that global emissions trading (cap-and-trade system) could be more complex and have higher upfront costs than the offsetting options, due to the need to administer aviation allowances. However, it should offer more flexibility for participants through the creation of additional emissions units, for example, an allowance, which can be traded in the marketplace. Auctioning allowances would create a revenue stream that could be used to mitigate the environmental impacts of aircraft engine emissions, including mitigation and adaptation, as well as assistance to and support for developing States, as per the guiding principle n) in Resolution A37-19, Annex.

As for implementing the scheme selected for recommendation to the 39th Session of the ICAO Assembly in 2016, the Report suggested three types of legal instruments as mechanisms that could implement a global MBM scheme: International treaties; Assembly Resolutions; and Standards contained in the Annexes to the Chicago Convention. The Report stated that legal instruments are not mutually exclusive and can be used in combination for the implementation of a global MBM scheme. According to the Report the advantage of an International Convention is that it would be binding upon Parties that ratify or accede to it. The execution of enforcement provisions could be facilitated under a Convention; however, it may take several years for the instrument to be adopted and even longer to enter into force. Should sufficient consensus exist among Member States of ICAO, a global MBM scheme may be developed through an Assembly Resolution. However, a Resolution would not be legally binding, which could complicate its enforcement. It would be challenging for Standards alone to manage all elements of a global MBM scheme. Standards could be useful tools in complementing other instruments by developing certain technical requirements of a global MBM scheme. These technical requirements may include rules for monitoring methodologies, fuel consumption reporting as well as recording, surrendering, cancelling and acquiring emissions units.

In early 2014, the ICAO Council, at its 201st Session considered a review[3] of Assembly Resolution A38-18 which reflected that an Action Plan for the development of a global MBM will be developed by ICAO by March 2014 and a first proposal for a global MBM scheme will be developed by June 2014.

Enforcement or Compliance?

Broadly, the recommendations of the Report in this regard are acceptable. Assembly Resolutions cannot require or even recommend that its principles be incorporated into national law or regulation. *Brownlie* has expressed the view that decisions by international conferences and organizations can in principle only bind those States accepting them (Brownlie 1990). Shaw, referring to the binding force of United Nations General; Assembly Resolutions states:

> ...one must be alive to the dangers in ascribing legal value to everything that emanates from the Assembly. Resolutions are often the results of political compromises and arrangements and, comprehended in that sense, never intended to constitute binding norms. Great care must be taken in moving from a plethora of practice to the identification of legal norms (Shaw 2003).

With regard to the practice of other international organizations, a little more caution might be required, as a resolution might create a custom. Non binding instruments form a special category that is sometimes referred to as "soft law" which is definitely not law in the sense of enforceability.[4] As for multilateral treaties, they are cumbersome in enforcing mandatory functions and obligations. Besides, conventions adopted under the auspices of ICAO, such as the aviation security Conventions have been a miserable failure. For instance, the text of the Protocol to the Tokyo Convention of 1963, which was to be considered by a diplomatic conference in April 2014 came 16 years after the Council requested work on the text. international treaties are woefully neglected by ICAO, a reality which is reflected by the fact that only twenty-nine Member States have signed the Beijing Convention 9 (with five ratifications and three accessions); only thirty-one Member States have signed the Protocol to the Beijing Convention (with five ratifications and two accessions) and only eleven Member States have ratified (with two accessions) the Convention on Compensation for Damage to Third Parties Resulting from Acts of Unlawful Interference Involving Aircraft (Unlawful interference Compensation Convention of 2009) and only 13 Member States have signed (with one accession) the Convention on Compensation for Damage Caused by Aircraft to Third Parties (General Risks Convention). Even the critical Convention for the Unification of Certain Rules for International Carriage by Air

---

[3] The review is contained in C-WP/14101, 15/01/14.

[4] Id. 111. See also A.J.P Tammes, *Decisions of International Organs as a Source of international Law*, 94 HR 1958 at 265.

(Montreal Convention of 1999) has been ratified by 104 Member States, leaving eighty-seven Member States still undecided.

That leaves the incorporation of a global MBM scheme as a Standard[5] in an Annex to the Chicago Convention. Here too ICAO will run into a problem. Article 37 of the Chicago Convention stipulates that each Contracting State undertakes to collaborate in securing the highest practicable degree of uniformity in regulations, standards, procedures, and organization in relation to aircraft, personnel, airways and auxiliary services in all matters in which such uniformity will facilitate and improve air navigation. To this end ICAO is required to adopt and amend from time to time, as may be necessary, international standards and recommended practices and procedures. However, Article 38 which immediately follows this requirement states that Any State which finds it impracticable to comply in all respects with any such international standard or procedure, or to bring its own regulations or practices into full accord with any international standard or procedure after amendment of the latter, or which deems it necessary to adopt regulations or practices differing in any particular respect from those established by an international standard, shall give immediate notification to the International Civil Aviation Organization of the differences between its own practice and that established by the international standard. In the case of amendments to international standards, any State which does not make the appropriate amendments to its own regulations or practices shall give notice to the Council within 60 days of the adoption of the amendment to the international standard, or indicate the action which it proposes to take. In any such case, the Council is required to make immediate notification to all other states of the difference which exists between one or more features of an international standard and the corresponding national practice of that State.

The conclusion therefore could be that an attempt at implementing an MBM scheme through an Assembly Resolution would be ineffective and impotent as States can always record a reservation and inveigle itself out of obligation. A multilateral treaty would be even more disastrous for two reasons: as history would show, ICAO might take another 15 years to come up with appropriate text for a

---

[5] Resolution A21-21 (Consolidated Statement of Continuing Policies and Associated Practices Related Specifically to Air Navigation), in Appendix A (Formulation of Standards and Recommended Practices and Procedures for Air Navigation Services) Resolves that a *Standard* is "any specification for physical characteristics, configuration, material, performance, personnel or procedure, the uniform application of which is recognized as necessary for the safety of international air navigation and to which Contracting States will conform in accordance with the Convention; in the event of impossibility of compliance, notification to the Council is compulsory under Article 38 of the Convention". The same Resolution defines a *Recommended Practice* as: "any specification for physical characteristics, configuration, material, performance, personnel or procedure, the uniform application of which is recognized as desirable in the interest of safety, regularity or efficiency of international air navigation and to which Contracting States will endeavour to conform in accordance with the Convention". These definitions are repeated verbatim in Assembly Resolution A37-15 in Appendix A (Formulation of Standards and Recommended Practices and Procedures for Air Navigation Services).

treaty; and even if it did, States could abstain from signing or ratifying such a treaty. As for a Standard in an Annex, Article 38 would give States who do not wish to adhere to a global MBM scheme the flexibility to record a difference, as discussed above. The only feasible discussion then would be to include a global MBM scheme as a Standard of Annex 2 (Rules of the Air) which is the only Annex to the Chicago Convention against which an ICAO member State cannot file a difference. Annex 2 derives its validity from Article 12 of the Convention relating to rules of the air.[6] In fact, it is very relevant that Annex 2, the responsibility for the promulgation of which devolves upon the Council by virtue of Article 54(1), sets mandatory rules of the air, making the existence of the legislative powers of the Council an unequivocal and irrefutable fact.

It is regrettable that the Report of the Assessment of Market Based Measures is dismissive of the most important aspect of introducing a global MBM scheme and that is the legal aspect of ensuring compliance. For the reasons given above, and the fact that ICAO has not been entirely successful in obtaining or ensuring adherence to multilateral treaties adopted under its patronage, the only way to go seems to be a mandatory scheme with oversight.

With regard to oversight of a global MBM's implementation, ICAO could address the feasibility of enlisting the help of its technical cooperation programme. ICAO is a specialized agency of the United Nations, deriving its legal legitimacy from Article 57[7] of the Charter of the United Nations (UN). The UN has established that four key principles should apply in the field of technical cooperation emanating from the UN. They are: (a) Lead responsibility for a given issue or activity should rest with the entity best equipped substantively to assume it; (b) Entities in the lead on a given issue or activity should work in close collaboration with the rest of the United Nations rather than attempt to duplicate expertise available elsewhere in the Organization; (c) More systematic efforts should be made to draw on the vast reservoir of knowledge and expertise that exists outside the United Nations system; and (d) Technical cooperation should be delivered to the maximum extent, possible by the entities that have an established field

---

[6] Article 12 stipulates that over the high seas, the rules in force shall be those established under the Convention, and each contracting State undertakes to insure the prosecution of all persons violating the applicable regulations.

[7] Article 57 stipulates that the various specialized agencies, established by intergovernmental agreement and having wide international responsibilities, as defined in their basic instruments, in economic, social, cultural, educational, health, and related fields, shall be brought into relationship with the United Nations in accordance with the provisions of Article 63. It also states that such agencies thus brought into relationship with the United Nations are hereinafter referred to as specialized agencies. Article 63 stipulates that The Economic and Social Council may enter into agreements with any of the agencies referred to in Article 57, defining the terms on which the agency concerned shall be brought into relationship with the United Nations. Such agreements shall be subject to approval by the General Assembly. It further states that the General Assembly may co-ordinate the activities of the specialized agencies through consultation with and recommendations to such agencies and through recommendations to the General Assembly and to the Members of the United Nations.

presence and experience. Secretariat entities should provide policy guidance and expertise, as appropriate.[8]

ICAO's role in these four key areas are rooted with the Council which directs the Organization (with the ultimate agreement of the Assembly) to deal with issues of particular concern i.e. matters pertaining to safety, security, environmental protection and the sustainable development of air transport. The genesis of ICAO's technical assistance, as related to the United Nations umbrella goes back to the Sixth Session of the Council in 1949 when it recognized a Resolution adopted by the UN Economic and Social Council (ECOSOC) in March 1948 which requested the UN Secretary General, in consultation with the executive heads of the interested specialized agencies to prepare a report setting forth a comprehensive plan for an expanded cooperative programme for economic development through the UN and its specialized agencies paying due attention to questions of a social nature which directly condition economic development and explore methods of financing such a programme including special budgets.[9]

The Council, in citing this ECOSOC Resolution observed that:

> In the interests of civil aviation alone, the Organization (ICAO) has an obligation to its member States to stand ready to extend assistance to the under developed countries. Any improvement in air navigation services helps to raise the levels of safety and efficiency on the international airlines...a proper response to such inquiries cannot be made by correspondence alone. It needs an early visit from a field office representative to discuss the needs with the officials of the State concerned and to make his own survey of the possibilities.[10]

This observation, made in 1949 by the Council, resonates well with the recent decision of the ICAO Secretary General to appoint dedicated technical cooperation officers in each of the ICAO regional offices.

The interoperability of technical assistance and technical cooperation within ICAO, particularly in the context of their separate definitions as discussed above, brings to bear the issue of funding. The question is, which activities would be funded by the regular programme, if any, and which activities would be funded through externally acquired resources from States for the specific purpose of rendering technical assistance? The President of the ICAO Council, at the 14th meeting of the Council in 1949 indicated that the principle he had in mind was that where extraordinary expenses were incurred, the first stages of the investigation and such small-scale assistance as could be given within a short space of time by

---

[8] Review of technical cooperation in the United Nations Report of the Secretary-General, Fifty-eighth session Agenda item 59, Strengthening of the United Nations system, A/58/382, 19 September 2003.

[9] C-WP/212 at Appendix B. The Council of ICAO recognized that other specialized agencies such as the Food and Agriculture Organization (FAO), the International Labour Organization (ILO), the World Health Organization (WHO) and the International Bank for Reconstruction and Development (IBRD better known as the World Bank) had already conducted technical assistance missions to member States. Id. Appendix C.

[10] C-WP/212 (1949) id. at 2.

ICAO's regular staff would be considered as a normal part of the work of the Organization, but that for anything that went beyond that the cost would be borne by the State benefitting or arranged through a joint project under Chapter XV of the Chicago Convention.[11] The Council noted that requests from States in this regard for ICAO assistance might take different forms. For instance, States could seek assistance in preparing a general programme of civil aviation; and for the development of air navigation facilities and services; they could seek specific advice on the planning and location of a particular facility such as an aerodrome; they may seek assistance in preparing detailed plans and specifications for the development and construction of particular projects or in letting contracts; they may seek advice as to the keeping of aeronautical statistics and other matters related to the economic activities of the Organization, or, on the drafting of civil navigation laws and other legal problems. Most important of all, States could seek advice on the establishment of personnel training programmes or even direct assistance in giving training.[12]

Worthy of note in the exercise pertaining to developing a global MBM scheme are three recommendations of Lord Stern in his 2006 Report alluded to earlier. They are:

- Putting a price on carbon. This can be achieved through tax or through trading mechanisms and will ensure that people are faced with the full social cost of their actions, leading individuals and businesses to prioritise and make informed choices on goods and services. This is particularly important for aviation, where significant growth is forecast and it is necessary to ensure that any increase in CO_2 from air travel is matched tonne-for-tonne by reductions elsewhere in the economy. The Report suggests that emissions trading can achieve that.
- The development and use of a wide range of low-carbon technologies is essential and urgent. The private sector plays a major role in R&D and technology diffusion, but closer collaboration between Government and industry would provide a further stimulus. Regulation will be necessary to force the pace of change.
- Barriers which prevent people from making informed decisions must be removed. Greener alternatives must be provided and their use actively encouraged. As well as good public transport and better urban design, there needs to be reliable information, labelling and sharing best practice to help people and businesses make sound decisions and stimulate markets for low carbon and high efficiency goods and services.[13]

---

[11] Doc 6684, C/766, 5/4/49 at 19.

[12] Id. Appendix B at 32.

[13] *Towards a Sustainable Transport System: Supporting Low Carbon Growth in a Low Carbon World*, UK Department of Transport, October 2007 at 9–10.

Key to these three points is the role of government which should adopt a robust air transport policy based on a proactive strategy that would enable the State to function within the parameters of a global environmental policy which would contribute to sustainable economic growth. Also, emissions reduction should go hand in hand with a global MBM where holding "stacks" at airports could be minimized; ASBUs are implemented; and slot allocation is closely linked to environmental protection.

If ICAO settles for a Standard within Annex 2 to the Chicago Convention, the problem of whether it can be enforceable will not go away, at least from an academic point of view. Although provisions of Annex 2 can be identified as binding principles of international law, most academics and professionals view international law as a "toothless tiger".[14] This means that collective enforcement through a system based on penalties, sanctions and compelling judicial processes play a tepid role. One commentator inquires:

> What is it that brings about states' compliance with international law? De Visscher points to "social conscience." But how is it that international law comes to reflect social conscience? Thomas Franck, in explaining why states obey "powerless rules," stresses the importance of legal legitimacy. Louis Henkin, who famously observed that "almost all states comply with almost all of international law almost all of the time," finds the explanation in states' interest in orderly relations.
>
> Ultimately, then, solving the puzzle of "voluntary" compliance presupposes a theory of compliance. Similarly, whether one sees the above-noted shift from enforcement to justification and judgment as recognition of the strength of international law or as admission of its weakness, depends in part upon the theoretical vantage point from which one contemplates the question.[15]

If therefore enforcement basically means the "act of compelling compliance with a law"[16] ICAO could, through a workable auditing and monitoring process compel compliance with a Standard in Annex 2.

In terms of monitoring compliance with a global MBM scheme ICAO can analogically draw on the concept of the high-level ICAO Secretariat Monitoring and Review Board (MARB) which has been established as part of an overall coordinated strategy for working with States that are found to have significant compliance shortcomings with respect to ICAO Standards and Recommended Practices (SARPs). The purpose of the MARB is to continue the work of the former Audit Results Review Board (ARRB) by focusing on developing and implementing broad, high-level assistance strategies. It will also focus on coordinating ICAO assistance and monitoring activities (the term monitoring in this document refers to both auditing and continuous monitoring activities), and on States with Significant Safety and/or Security Concerns.

---

[14] See generally, Jutta Brunnee, Enforcement Mechanisms in International Law and International Environmental Law, *Ensuring Compliance with Multilateral Environmental Agreements: A Dialogue between Practitioners and Academia* (2005) at 2.

[15] Id. at 5.

[16] *Black's Law Dictionary* 8th ed.:2004, at 569, cited in *Brunnee*, supra note 288 at 3.

The MARB is an ICAO Secretariat senior management forum responsible for:

(a) coordinating and evaluating the effectiveness and efficiency of monitoring activities to ensure that opportunities for continuous improvement are identified and acted upon; and

(b) identifying, coordinating and validating assistance strategies and other courses of action to improve the responsiveness of States to ICAO monitoring activities and to address identified needs.

The MARB examines both the safety and security histories of specific States and provides an internal advisory forum for coordination among ICAO's safety, security and assistance programmes. There is no reason such a mechanism or a similar mechanism cannot be extended to monitoring environmental compliance as well.

References

Brownlie I (1990) Principles of public international law, 4th edn. Clarendon Press, Oxford, p 691
Shaw MN (2003) International law, 5th edn. Cambridge University Press, Cambridge, p 110

Chapter 8
Mitigating the Environmental Impact: The ICAO Role

A significant consideration that is intrinsically linked to the search of a global MBM is contained in Resolution A38-18 which states in its Annex *inter alia*, that:

> n) where revenues are generated from MBMs, it is strongly recommended that they should be applied in the first instance to mitigating the environmental impact of aircraft engine emissions, including mitigation and adaptation, as well as assistance to and support for developing States

This essentially means that funds collected should be used for research and development of new technology as well as capacity development and resource funding for States mostly in need of such assistance. The increasing dependency of aviation on fossil fuels, which was exacerbated by the fuel price crisis of 2008, has brought to bear the need to consider the use of alternative fuels in the industry. In this regard, ICAO convened the Conference on Aviation and Alternative Fuels (CAAF) at Rio de Janeiro in Brazil from 16 to 18 November 2009. The Conference was a major event showcasing the state of the art in aviation alternative fuels, and an event at which a Global Framework for Aviation Alternative Fuels (GFAAF)[1] was considered. The GFAAF was designed as a living document that will be continually updated on the ICAO website that will share information, best practices and future initiatives by ICAO Member States and the air transport industry. The Conference made reference to the High-Level Meeting on

---

[1] See ICAO Doc CAAF/09-WP/23, 18/11/09.

© The Author(s) 2014
R. Abeyratne, *Aviation and Climate Change*, SpringerBriefs in Law,
DOI: 10.1007/978-3-319-08443-5_8

International Aviation and Climate Change[2] convened earlier by ICAO which recommended that States and International Organizations actively participate in CAAF with a view to sharing their efforts and strategies to promote such work and to update the 15th Meeting of the Conference of the Parties to the United Nations Framework Convention on Climate Change (UNFCC COP15) which was held in December 2009)[3].

The Conference adopted a Declaration which recognized the urgent need for measures to facilitate access to financial resources, technology exchange, and capacity building specific to aviation alternative fuels and acknowledged that the demand for sustainable fuels extends beyond international aviation, but that aircraft have unique fuel specification requirements It also recognized the need to encourage supply chain stakeholders to ensure that sustainable alternative fuels are made available to aviation and acknowledged that with sufficient incentive and supply, international aviation could deliver a substantial CO_2 reduction benefit from the use of sustainable alternative fuels for aircraft and that, due to its small network of fuel distribution points and its predictable demand international aviation is well suited to becoming a global first adopter of sustainable alternative fuels.

The Declaration recommended that: ICAO and its Member States endorse the use of sustainable alternative fuels for aviation, particularly the use of drop-in fuels in the short to mid-term, as an important means of reducing aviation emissions; ICAO establish a Global Framework for Aviation Alternative Fuels (GFAAF) on aviation and sustainable alternative fuels to communicate what individual and shared efforts expect to achieve with sustainable alternative fuels for aviation in the future for consideration by the 37th Session of the ICAO Assembly. The GFAAF will be continually updated Member States and stakeholders work together through ICAO and other relevant international bodies, to exchange

---

[2] The High Level Meeting on Aviation and Climate Change, convened by the International Civil Aviation Organization from 7 to 9 October 2009 once again brought to bear the vexed issue of ICAO's leadership in the field, only to be re-endorsed by the 56 States which attended the Meeting, that ICAO was indeed the leader and that ICAO should provide guidance on various issues pertaining to the subject. The meeting went on to acknowledge the principles and provisions on common but differentiated responsibilities and respective capabilities, and the fact that developed countries will be taking the lead under the UNFCCC and the Kyoto Protocol. It also acknowledged the principles of non-discrimination and equal and fair opportunities to develop international aviation set forth in the Chicago Convention and re-emphasized the vital role which international aviation plays in global economic and social development and the need to ensure that international aviation continues to develop in a sustainable manner.

[3] At the United Nations Framework Convention on Climate Change 15th Meeting of the Conference of the Parties (COP15) and the Fifth Meeting of the Parties to the Kyoto Protocol (CMP5) which were convened in Copenhagen on 8 December 2009, leaders from the U.S., India, Brazil, South Africa and China came to an agreement to combat global warming. The deal, which was only between five countries, contained no specifics on emissions cuts, but it did commit the countries to look to keep global warming at 2 °C or less and to promise $30 billion in funding to battle climate change by 2012. It also created a framework for international transparency on climate actions for developed and developing nations alike.

information and best practices, and in particular to reach a common definition of sustainability requirements for alternative fuels; Member States are encouraged to work together expeditiously with the industry to foster the research, development, deployment and usage of sustainable alternative fuels for aviation; Funding efforts that support the study and development of sustainable alternative fuels and other measures to reduce GHG emissions, in addition to the funding for research and technology programmes to further improve the efficiency of air transport, be maintained or improved; Member States are encouraged to establish policies that support the use of sustainable alternative aviation fuels, ensure that such fuels are available to aviation and avoid unwanted or negative side effects, which could compromise the environmental benefits of alternative fuels; The ICAO Council should further elaborate on measures to assist developing States as well as to facilitate access to financial resources, technology transfer and capacity building; There is an urgent need for measures to facilitate access to financial resources, technology exchange, and capacity building specific to sustainable aviation alternative fuels; ICAO takes the necessary steps with the aim of considering a framework for financing infrastructure development projects dedicated to sustainable aviation alternative fuels and incentives to overcome initial market hurdles; ICAO continue to facilitate efforts to develop a lifecycle analysis framework for comparing the relative GHG emissions from sustainable alternative fuels to the lifecycle of conventional fuels for aviation; and ICAO and its Member States should strongly encourage wider discussions on the development of alternative fuel technologies and support the use of sustainable alternative fuels, including biofuels, in aviation in accordance with national circumstances.

The establishment of GFAAF was part of a Declaration adopted at the Rio Conference, which recognized that the introduction of sustainable alternative fuels for aviation will help to address issues of environment, economics, and supply security, and noted *the* very limited availability of qualified alternative fuels for aviation as well as the fact that sustainable alternative fuels for aircraft can be produced from a wide variety of feedstocks for use in global aviation. The Declaration suggested that many regions are candidate production locations and acknowledged that sustainable alternative fuels for aviation may offer reduced lifecycle CO_2 emissions compared to the lifecycle of conventional aviation fuels. It also acknowledged that sustainable alternative fuels for aviation may also offer benefits to surface and local air quality. While the Declaration noted that the technology existed to produce substitute, sustainable fuels for aviation that took into consideration worlds food security, energy and sustainable development needs, it was recognized that the production of sustainable alternative fuels for aviation could promote new economic opportunities.

At the United Nations Framework Convention on Climate Change 15th Meeting of the Conference of the Parties (COP15) and the Fifth Meeting of the Parties to the Kyoto Protocol (CMP5) which were convened in Copenhagen on 8 December 2009, leaders from the U.S., India, Brazil, South Africa and China came to an agreement to combat global warming. The deal, which was only between five countries, contained no specifics on emissions cuts, but it did commit the countries to look to keep global warming at 2 °C or less and to promise $30 billion in funding to battle climate change by 2012. It also created a framework for international transparency on climate actions for developed and developing nations alike.

Funding Technology

During the 31st Session of the ICAO Assembly in September 1995, eight members of The Latin American Civil Aviation Commission (LACAC) presented their proposals for the setting up of an aeronautical monetary fund for the benefit of the aviation community Citing the reason for the proposal as the difficulties faced by governments and airlines to obtain financing at reasonable costs for the modernization of airlines, airport infrastructure, air traffic services and navigation aids, LACAC introduced the proposal as a means to contribute to the balanced development of international air transport.

LACAC, at its Panel meeting on 13–14 June 1994 held in Salvador, Brazil, proposed the inauguration of the fund to finance air navigation services provided by the satellite based Communications, Navigation, Surveillance/Air Traffic Management (CNS/ATM) system. It was the consensus in LACAC that the fund should be created by international agreement, and that the entity which would receive and administer the financing of the CNS/ATM system under the fund should be an international bank established for that purpose. The overriding principle of the aeronautical monetary fund remained, however, that its administration should be supervised by ICAO.

The LACAC initiative was in response to the introduction of satellite technology to future air navigation systems which ICAO has been energetically involved in since 1993. These new air navigation systems would be operated through a satellite network dedicated to the air transport industry. In order to ensure such an exclusive dedication to air transport users of a satellite system, the costs that have to be incurred would also be substantial. These costs that would enable the transition of air navigation from currently used navigation systems to satellite technology would have to be absorbed by a funding source in order that an efficient and effective CNS/ATM system be implemented globally.

The objective of the fund, according to LACAC, was to provide the financial resources necessary to meet the most pressing needs of LACAC member States for the construction and modernization of airport infrastructure, air traffic services and navigation aids. Also included in the list of beneficiaries were airline fleets which needed expansion and modernization.

LACAC proposed that the fund be created through an international Convention open to ICAO Contracting States. The Convention would necessitate adherence by States if their airlines, airports and other initiatives were to benefit from the fund. The fund would be totally autonomous and politically independent from the control of individual or collective governments.

The money that formed the fund was to come from the user—the airline—and any other interested financial institution and would be collected semi-annually in accordance with procedure agreed upon between the parties to the Convention.

It was also proposed that the fund be administered by a Board of Governors (one appointed by each member government), five Executive Directors elected by the Board and a Managing Director who should ideally be a senior member of the International banking community and elected by the Executive Directors. The administration of the fund included audit of accounts to be carried out annually by a specialized international firm of accountants. Inherent in the audit principles was a proposal for absolute transparency devoid of diplomatic immunity and commercial confidentiality.

The advantage of the fund was identified by LACAC primarily as self sufficiency. Other advantages were the improvement of air navigation facilities worldwide by both the developed and developing world, and the possibility of making available credit facilities through the fund to civil aviation bodies and the air transport industry. The most significant feature of the LACAC proposal was that the aeronautical monetary fund would act as a tool which would promote the implementation of ICAO's Strategic Action Plan, which was the precursor to the current Business Plan of the Organization.

Implied in the proposal was the incontrovertible fact that the Strategic Action Plan cannot be implemented unilaterally by ICAO without the cooperation of its member States. Fundamentally, and from a legal standpoint, the position of ICAO in the international aviation community is not one that is compatible with being absolutely legislative in capacity. ICAO sets guidelines on civil aviation and facilitates the adoption of treaties and regulations, with the approval of its member States. It is then up to the member States themselves to implement them. The SAP was therefore essentially a two sided issue and could have been adequately subsumed in the adage "one cannot clap with one hand". It was also claimed that the obligations of ICAO member States were are paramount in giving teeth to ICAO's Standards and Recommended Practices and other guidelines, as much as in satisfying or otherwise accepting treaties of air law that they themselves have adopted under ICAO auspices.

The LACAC proposal therefore suggested that it was essential for ICAO contracting States to recognise the compelling need to address the issue of the establishment of the aeronautical monetary fund in the context of its supportive role in financing on a global scale the key elements of the Strategic Action Plan.

Also at the 31st Session of the ICAO Assembly, Contracting States adopted Assembly Resolution A31-2 (Increasing the effectiveness of ICAO) which called for ICAO's the Strategic Action Plan to be "updated and rolled forward" at least triennially. Following a comprehensive overview by the ICAO Secretariat, the Council on 12 June 2000 adopted revised text for the Plan which, *inter alia* updated the original Plan to address long-term strategic objectives, including the introduction of the *Universal Safety Oversight Audit Programme* of ICAO and consideration of its development with a view to its expansion to cover all safety-related Annexes to the Chicago Convention.

Although the Executive Committee of the 31st ICAO Assembly, which considered the LACAC proposal, had great sympathy for the objectives of the proposal it was generally noted that the establishment of an international Convention was both a complex and time consuming undertaking needing careful thought and detailed consideration of the issues involved before it attains fruition. While some members of the Committee recommended the consideration of more innovative financial instruments to realize funding for CNS/ATM, others, such as the observer for IATA, strongly opposed the proposal on the grounds that it was inconsistent with ICAO policies to create a fund which was financed by users of civil aviation.

The Committee concluded that the proposal for the creation of an International aeronautical Monetary Fund was laudable, and indeed, a valuable one but thought it fit to leave it to the ICAO Council to decide how best the proposal should be pursued further. The ICAO Council, following the position taken by the ICAO Assembly at its 31st Session, requested the Secretariat to study the proposal further. Consequently, a preliminary Study was conducted by the Secretariat and considered by the 32nd Session of the ICAO Assembly in 1998. Flowing from the request of the Assembly at this session, for a more detailed study of the subject by the Secretariat, a further Study was prepared, and was placed before the ICAO Council.

The IFFAS Analogy

The Council Working Group which was subsequently established, decided that the fund to be established be called International Financial Facility for Aviation Safety (IFFAS). At an early stage, the Working Group sought to clarify the nature of IFFAS. Was it to be a "mechanism", a bank, some other corporate body, a fund? Relevant to this was its relationship to ICAO as it presently exists. Given that IFFAS was to be operated under the ICAO legal regime, it was considered that it could not have separate corporate legal status. But since it was to be operated independently of ICAO's Regular Budget, the means of distinguishing IFFAS from the rest of the Organization needed to be identified.

The Group concluded that IFFAS would have four components: participants, a fund, a Governing Body, and staff. The first would be donors and/or beneficiaries, the second would be the voluntarily–provided finance both for funding projects in States and for running IFFAS itself, the third would be those responsible for running the Facility and deciding which projects to fund and on what terms, and the last would be those needed to assist the Governing Body to carry out its tasks.

Participation

Taking Resolution A33-10 as its guideline, the Group determined that IFFAS should be open to the voluntary participation of Contracting States and other parties as identified in the text of the Assembly Resolution. There was considerable discussion of whether there should be a minimum contribution, and how potential beneficiary States who, by definition, would be short of resources might participate. As a result of these discussions, Article V of the draft Administrative Charter draws some distinctions between participants, contributors and possible beneficiaries.

Loans and/or Grants

The philosophy of IFFAS was based on provision of assistance to States, as is n) of Annex to Resolution A38-18 alluded to earlier in this chapter. Therefore it is relevant that some members of the IFFAS Working Group noted that for IFFAS to be a loan making facility it would need to address a whole series of issues on the credit-worthiness of the beneficiaries, interest rates, appropriate repayment periods, bad debts, etc. These would be avoided if it provided only grants. The latter approach would also recognise the likelihood that the beneficiaries, at least in the early days, would be States who had been unable to pay their ICAO minimum rate contributions, and thus were bound to find it difficult to meet a schedule of repayments. On the other hand, it was argued that the Facility should be designed to be self sustaining, and that beneficiary States were likely to feel a greater commitment to a project financed by loan. Having considered the merits of the two approaches at length, the Working Group decided, in keeping with principles contained in Resolution A33-10, to ascribe to IFFAS the primary function of disbursing loans. However, it was the view of the Working Group that IFFAS should include the flexibility of awarding grants or zero interest loans when the Governing Body deems it appropriate and necessary. To this effect the draft Administrative Charter at Attachment 1 contains provisions that will enable the Governing Body, notwithstanding the primary IFFAS characteristic of granting loans at concessional interest rates, to award grants and zero interest loans in certain circumstances.

Relationship to ICAO and Associated Liability

Resolution A33-10 was quite clear (Resolving Clause 2) in endorsing the concept of an IFFAS with "complete independence from ICAO's Programme Budget", and "provision of any administrative or other services by ICAO only upon request by participating States and on a cost recovery basis". While the only reference to the "existing ICAO legal regime" appears in the context of creating a management strategy for the structure of IFFAS that is in conformity with that regime—i.e. a strategy that fits but does not itself necessarily fall within the ICAO regime—the Working Group accepted advice from the Legal Bureau that, as a practical matter, it will both simplify and expedite the setting up of IFFAS to create it within ICAO.

By comparison with an independent body set up outside the Organization, this brought additional factors into play, since the issue of complete independence from ICAO's Programme Budget becomes an internal administrative matter. In short, while the Council could devolve various tasks on the IFFAS Governing Body, the Council and ultimately the Contracting States it represented could not avoid taking responsibility for whatever may be done by or in the name of an IFFAS which was to be part of ICAO. In practical terms this probably would not have produced an onerous burden, but the essence of IFFAS is that ICAO was stepping into new territory, of which the Organization has had no direct experience. It will be a matter for the Governing Body to examine this issue more extensively and report to the Council.

The Working Group accordingly focused attention on the possible liabilities and associated costs that might accrue to ICAO as a direct or indirect consequence of the conduct of IFFAS–related activities. Experience has shown that even where ICAO might be expected to be protected by its international immunities, it has found it necessary to spend funds to meet legal and other costs resulting from claims which might never be sustained on their merits. Although this experience related to the area of implementation, and it may well be that in a funding situation such liability may not arise, there is no reason to suppose that the limitation of the IFFAS role effectively to that of a financier will guarantee ICAO's exclusion from such claims, well founded or otherwise, in respect of IFFAS activities.

In this context, the Working Group considered how ICAO could best be protected, whether by insurance or some other appropriate indemnification, guaranty or surety arrangement. It concluded that the nature and extent of arrangements to ensure that ICAO was adequately protected from claims resulting from IFFAS–related activities was a matter for the Governing Body to decide, subject to the approval of the Council, as an element of the Governing Body's ordinary duty of care. Enquiries made of some major multilateral investment and lending institutions indicate that those institutions do not normally carry insurance to cover all of their potential legal liabilities. In those cases, however, the institutions retain sufficient funds in reserve to protect against such contingencies, and they generally maintain the right to call on contributors to underwrite such expenses, if and when they arise, up to the value of each donor's financial commitment. As contributions to IFFAS are entirely voluntary, it will not be possible to obtain such commitments. In the circumstances, the Working Group recommends that, based on reliable and authoritative assessments of the nature and extent of the liabilities to which ICAO could reasonably expect to be exposed as a result of IFFAS-related activities, appropriate measures to protect ICAO's funds, assets and resources must be in place.

Roles of the Council, the Secretary General, and the IFFAS Governing Body

The Working Group found this a delicate area. The Assembly Resolution clearly contemplated an IFFAS that would be considerably removed from the day to day interest of the Council. It contemplated no specific role for the Secretary General, merely referring to the cost recovery basis for any ICAO services provided. At the same time, the inclusion of IFFAS within the overall structure of ICAO meant the relationships between the three institutions cannot be ignored.

The Group focused primarily on the tasks of the Governing Body, since it is the functioning of that body which embodies the essence of IFFAS. Those tasks are embodied in Article VI of the Administrative Charter of IFFAS, with elaboration of them in Appendices B to D of Attachment 1. Appendix B contains general guidelines for the provision of loans and grants from IFFAS, Appendix C reflects principles to be followed in the investment management of IFFAS, and Appendix D lays down principles upon which the Governing Body and staff of IFFAS would be constituted and function. These appendices reflect principles developed by the Working Group to ensure a proper balance between prudent financial and investment management and the efficient use of available resources. These principles will be given further emphasis and elaboration in a compendium for IFFAS to be developed along the time line suggested in Appendix B of Attachment 3.

The Study Group's Strategy

The Council Study Group based its considerations on Resolution A33-10 (Establishment of an International Financial Facility for Aviation Safety (IFFAS)), in particular, clause 2 which endorses the concept of an IFFAS, and (clause 3 d) which provided that IFFAS should be established on the basis of a transparent and simple management mechanism with special attention paid to measures to assure quality control and to assess effectiveness and efficiency at all levels (clause 3 d) (5) and provisions for the auditing of accounts (clause 3 d) 6). The Council Study Group also acknowledged the link between Resolution A33-10 and Resolution A33-9 (Resolving deficiencies identified by the Universal Safety Oversight Audit Programme and encouraging quality assurance for technical co-operation projects) particularly clause 2. Also noted by the Council Study Group in this context was the requirement in Resolution A33-10 that an IFFAS should have a management strategy developed on the principles of, and in conformity with, the existing ICAO legal regime (clause 3 c). The Council Study Group observed, in this context, the relevance of provisions contained in Chapter XV of the Convention on International Civil Aviation, in particular Articles 69 and 70, which formed the legal basis for ICAO involvement in IFFAS. These principles, together with clause 7 of Resolution A33-10, which required the Council to provide information to the

Assembly on the progress of IFFAS, confirmed that some degree of oversight of the Council was necessary.

It was the view of the Council Study Group that, of paramount importance to the establishment of IFFAS were principles enshrined in clause 2 (b) of Resolution A33-10, in particular those reflecting voluntary participation by States and complete independence of IFFAS from the Programme Budget of ICAO.

It was also the view of the Council Study Group that, in order to assist the Council in deciding on the most effective, efficient and transparent structure of administration of IFFAS, some information on the functions of development banks (notably the Inter-American Development Bank (IDB), African Development Bank (AFDB), Islamic Development Bank (IDB) and Asian Development Bank (ADB)) would be of use.

Strategy for the Establishment of IFFAS

Given the above considerations, the Council Study Group recommended to the Council that the primary task in formulating a structure for IFFAS would be to identify an appropriate strategy through which IFFAS could best serve its objective and purpose. The impact of IFFAS on the market (i.e. supply and demand) would largely depend on an efficient structure which should be formulated by taking into account an appropriate legal basis and structure for IFFAS based on the principles of Resolution A33-10, in particular, clauses 2 and 3 (b) and Chapter XV of the Convention on International Civil Aviation, Articles 69 and 70, efficient financial management, quality assurance and audit and sustainable development of the Facility.

Throughout discussions in the Council, the idea of global application of principles on a regional basis was favoured. With this in mind, the ICAO Secretariat had already taken some steps in the global promotion of IFFAS through workshops, seminars and other meetings which ICAO organizes or participates in the regions and, through this process, many States have been sensitized to IFFAS. The regional applicability of IFFAS will be in cooperation with regional financial institutions and such regional bodies as the African Civil Aviation Commission (AFCAC), European Civil Aviation Conference (ECAC) and Latin American Civil Aviation Commission (LACAC).

As for ICAO Secretariat support for the IFFAS, it was recommended that initially the IFFAS Secretariat would consist of one or two officers. These officers could be provided by the Secretariat to perform IFFAS-related tasks in addition to their substantive duties on a full cost-recovery basis. It was not envisioned that this would be a major burden on IFFAS funds. It was emphasized that throughout the existence of IFFAS, the Secretariat structure supporting IFFAS should be lean, so as not to impose a heavy financial burden on IFFAS assets.

It was the view of the Council that, once a structure for the Facility is identified, the Council may wish to consider development of appropriate legal documentation incorporating in detail the manner and form of implementing an IFFAS mechanism.

Based on the above, the Council Study Group decided to recommend to the Council that it consider Appendix A (which contained text of a draft Administrative Charter for IFFAS) in the context of pursuing the establishment of an IFFAS within the parameters of Resolution A33-10. To this end, the Council Study Group recommended that the Council work toward establishing a workable and viable IFFAS and that consideration by the Council of Appendix A should be a well thought out and circumspect exercise, given that the Council was only required to pursue the establishment of an IFFAS at that stage. The Council Study Group suggested that the Council consider the advantages of establishing a provisional IFFAS initially to provide financing for certain safety-related projects identified through universal safety oversight audit programme (USOAP) (indicative projects in Appendix C), based on a practical system of funding. A progress report of such a provisional facility may enable the Council to make appropriate recommendations to the Assembly regarding the establishment of IFFAS in the long term.

Responsibility of ICAO for Running a Funding Facility

The seminal principle which mandates ICAO as the Organization responsible for the international regulation of civil aviation is found in Article 44 (a) of the Chicago Convention which requires the Organization to insure the safe and orderly growth of international civil aviation throughout the world. The word "insure" devolves upon ICAO the responsibility to make absolutely certain that international civil aviation grows safely and in an orderly manner. ICAO is also required, by Article 44(d), to meet the needs of the peoples of the world for safe, regular, efficient and economical air transport. Therefore, there is no room for doubt that the Contracting States of ICAO, by the Chicago Convention itself, will hold ICAO accountable for ensuring safety and efficiency in air transport. Article 54(i) of the Chicago Convention authorizes the Council to request, collect, examine and publish information relating to the advancement of air navigation and the operation of international air services, including information about the costs of operation and particulars of subsidies paid to airlines from public funds. This provision enables the ICAO Council to make an exhaustive study of the financial outlay needed for the 185 Contracting States of ICAO to implement not only the CNS/ATM system but also related programmes such as safety oversight which is often dependent on the availability of proper air navigation facilities and training in the States concerned.

The Council of ICAO has, on occasion, focussed its attention on ICAO's possible legal duties and liabilities along with immunities accruing to the Organization, particularly when considering ICAO's role as supervisor or administrator of certain projects. One such project was IFFAS which brought into issue ICAO's role assigned by the Administrative Charter of IFFAS as coming within the legal umbrella of ICAO. The other project is the Public Key Directory (PKD) which ICAO oversees, supervise and administer on behalf of a group of owner States whereby certain data is encoded and decoded to ascertain the integrity of the e-passport. In discussing both these issues the Council vehemently inquired into the possible legal liabilities of the Organization. Although this issue would come to a head only when ICAO is made a litigant by an aggrieved party and the courts are charged with determining ICAO's status as a litigant in a national jurisdiction, given the rapidly evolving role of ICAO, it is opportune to view the Organization's reception as a litigant in national courts.

ICAO Before the Courts

Since IFFAS was an instrumentality of ICAO operating under ICAO's legal umbrella, the first step was to determine ICAO's legal status. Although a precise definition did not exist, it could not be doubted that ICAO or any other international organization could be delimited and delineated. The most fundamental delimitation lies in the body of law that governs the Organization. ICAO is primarily governed by international law, being recognized by the United Nations Charter as a specialized agency of the United Nations. It is also governed by two major agreements, one between the United Nations and ICAO and the other between the Government of Canada and ICAO. Both accord the organization legal legitimacy sufficient for a common law court to follow the principle enunciated in the House of Lords in the 1995 case of *Arab Monetary Fund* v. *Hashim* that:

> English law will only recognize a foreign entity as having legal personality and therefore a capacity to sue or be sued if such body has been accorded legal personality under the law of a foreign State recognized by this country...[4]

This principle was followed in the United States in a continuation of the case pursuant to the defendant taking up domicile in the United States and filing action for bankruptcy before the Arab Monetary Fund could bring an action against him. The bankruptcy court judge followed the reasoning of the House of Lords and held that, while recognizing that although the United States was not a member of the Arab Monetary Fund, and therefore the fund could not be subjected to the national court's jurisdiction, nonetheless the Fund was a juridical person under United Arab Emirates law and therefore its capacity would flow to the United States under customary international law. The basic issue regarding ICAO's legal status lies in Article 44 of the Chicago Convention, which recognizes that ICAO's aims and objectives are to develop the principles and techniques of international air navigation and to foster the planning and development of international air transport so

---

[4] 213 F.3d 1169 at 1172; 2000 U.S. App. LEXIS 11897.

as to, *inter alia*, meet the needs of the peoples of the world for safe, regular, efficient and economical air transport. This general proviso is qualified by Article 37 of the Convention which provides that ICAO shall adopt and amend from time to time, as may be necessary, international standards and recommended practices and procedures.

The second issue was, can ICAO be recognized as having legal capacity, firstly in Canada, which is home to ICAO and secondly in any of ICAO's member States. The Headquarters Agreement between ICAO and Canada, in Article 2, explicitly provides that ICAO shall possess juridical personality and shall have the legal capacities of a body corporate including the capacity to contract; to acquire and dispose of movable and immovable property; and to institute legal proceedings. With regard to the question as to whether ICAO can be sued in Canada, Article 3 of the Agreement provides that the Organization, its property and its assets, wherever located and by whomsoever held, shall enjoy the same immunity from suit and every form of judicial process as is enjoyed by foreign states. Canada's recognition of ICAO having legal capacities of a body corporate is consistent with Article 104 of the United Nations Charter which provides that the United Nations shall enjoy in the territory of each of its member States such legal capacity as may be necessary for the exercise of its functions and the fulfilment of its purposes. The question which naturally arose from these provisions is "what effect does the Headquarters Agreement between ICAO and the Government of Canada have as a legally enforceable document before the local courts"? In the 1988 *Applicability of the Obligation to Arbitrate Case* where the International Court of Justice had to consider whether United States anti-terrorism legislation necessitated the closure of the Palestine Liberation Organization's observer mission to the UN in New York, the Court held that the United States was obligated to respect its obligation, contained in Article 21 of the UN Headquarters Agreement with the United States, that the United States had to enter into arbitration in case of a dispute on the interpretation of the Agreement. The court laid particular emphasis on the fact that provisions of a treaty must prevail over the domestic law of a State Party to that treaty. Therefore, there is no room for doubt that ICAO is able to conduct business both in Canada and in the territories of any of its member States as a juridical person.

ICAO's Immunities and Liabilities

At customary international law, the position of an international organization regarding immunity from suit and other judicial process is unclear and falls within applicable treaty provision, such as the United Nations Charter, Article 105 of which clearly stipulates that the United Nations Organization shall enjoy in the territory of each of its members such privileges and immunities as are necessary for the fulfilment of its purposes. Immunities of the United Nations system are also addressed in the *General Convention on the Privileges and Immunities of the*

United Nations of 1946, which sheds some light as to the rights and liabilities of the United Nations and its various entities. ICAO's legal liability within Canada may well hinge on the recognition by the Canadian government that ICAO shall enjoy the same immunity from suit and every form of judicial process as is enjoyed by foreign States. Should the matter of ICAO's immunity be brought before a court within Canada, it might well look into the true worth of the statement.

Immunity of foreign States in a local jurisdiction has undergone an interesting metamorphosis, from the recognition of personal sovereignty to acceptance of more abstract concepts of State sovereignty. The immunity accorded to ICAO by Canada would impute to the Organization the independence and equality of a State, which municipal courts would be reluctant to impugn or question unless with the consent of ICAO. Principles of sovereign immunity go back to the early 19th century where the jurisdiction of a State was recognized as being mutually exclusive from the Sovereign immunity of a State. In the well known *Pinochet* case (2000), Lord Browne-Wilkinson observed that it was a basic principle of international law that one sovereign state (the forum state) does not adjudicate on the conduct of a foreign state. The foreign state is entitled to procedural immunity from the processes of the forum state. The immunity applies both to criminal as well as civil liability. English law is quite clear on the above proposition and is best illustrated by the point made by Lord Millett in the case of *Holland* v. *Lampen-Wolfe*[5] decided in 2000 that:

> State immunity...is a creature of customary international law and derives from the equality of sovereign states. It is not a self imposed restriction on the jurisdiction of its courts which the United Kingdom has chosen to adopt. It is a limitation imposed from without upon the sovereignty of the United Kingdom itself.

Immunity from jurisdiction of the courts does not mean exemption from the legal system of the State in which the Organization resides. Although the two concepts are similar and the former meant that the courts had to respect the sovereignty of foreign states, it was merely a procedural tenet that could not always impugn the constitutional roots of an internal legal system.

It must be noted that international and domestic instruments implicitly prohibit sovereign immunity in cases of tortious liability involving civil wrongs. The Canadian *State Immunity Act* of 1982, in Section 6, allows for compensation for civil wrongs caused in Canada, resulting in death, damage to tangible property or personal injury. An analogy can be observed in the *European Convention on State Immunity* of 1972, which in Article 11 admits of redress for injury to the person or damage to tangible property, if the facts which occasioned the injury or damage occurred in the territory of the forum, and if the author of the injury or damage was present at the time of the act. Similarly, The United Kingdom *State Immunity Act*, in Section 5, provides that a State is not immune in respect of proceedings relating

---

[5] 1 WLR 1573; (2000) UKHRR 734.

to death or personal injury, or damage to or loss of tangible property, caused by an act or omission in the United Kingdom.

The conceptual basis for granting international organizations immunity regarding their professional activities was well brought out in the 1983 case of *Mendaro* v. *the World Bank*[6] where the US Court of Appeal held that the reason for granting immunities to an international organization is to enable them to pursue their functions more effectively and particularly to permit organizations to operate unfettered by unilateral control of a State over activities conducted within its territory. In *Iran-US Claims Tribunal* v. *AS*[7] The Dutch Supreme Court acknowledged that immunity in its absolute form gives an international organization a guarantee that it could perform its functions without being controlled by domestic policy and law. The Swiss Labor Court held in *ZM* v. *Permanent Delegation of the League of Arab States to the UN*[8] that it is incontrovertibly at customary international law that international organizations, whether universal or regional, enjoy absolute jurisdictional immunity and that they can only carry out their tasks assigned to them if they were not deprived of this immunity.

The above discussion seemingly establishes that jurisdictional immunity is awarded to international organizations as a matter of course. The real issue however, with respect to immunity, particularly that of ICAO as recognized by the Government of Canada, is the extent to which immunity will be granted as per existing norms of international law. The Headquarters agreement between ICAO and Canada merely stipulates that ICAO will have the same immunity from suit and every form of judicial process as is enjoyed by foreign States. The operative question is "what is the immunity that is enjoyed by foreign States in Canada in this context?" Is it an absolute form of immunity or a qualified immunity? This brings to bear the relevance of early doctrinaire distinctions drawn by jurisdictions of Belgium and Italy, where courts recognized two forms of immunity based on the type of activity carried out. The first applied to sovereign acts of a government or *jure imperii* and the second applied to acts of a commercial nature or *jure gestionis*. This distinctive approach, often referred to as the doctrine of restrictive or relative immunity, is applied unreservedly by courts of many countries while others, including Canada, apply the restrictive immunity doctrine only in principle.

The approach taken by courts to acts of sovereign authority and acts of a private character in the context of restrictive immunity will largely depend on whether the act in question was a commercial act performed on the basis of a private relationship such as a contract. Another criterion might well be whether an act in question was performed on behalf of a State or Organization by an individual. Courts in Australia and the United Kingdom have used three methods to determine the extent of immunity that should be granted: consideration as to whether granting a general immunity from jurisdiction is justified; creating a list of specific

---

[6] 717 F.2d 610 (1983).

[7] Claim No. A/30.

[8] Geneva Labour Court, 17 November 1993, *ILR* 643.

immunities and detailed exceptions; and refusal of immunity in instances where the property of a foreign state has been used for commercial purposes. The United States courts have held that some acts deserve exclusive and absolute immunity, such as internal administrative acts, diplomatic activity and the grant of public loans. In the 1988 case *International Tin Council* v. *Amalgamet Inc.*,[9] The plaintiff ITC averred that it was not obliged to go in for arbitration on the ground that it was an international organization and action under the litigation was perfomed by the plaintiff as an act of State. The court found this argument untenable as it could not find a "sovereign"character in the contract in question. This decision can be distinguished from the ICAO situation as the ITC had not been given the status of a foreign States as has ICAO under its agreement with Canada.

Waiver of Immunity

There are instances where the courts might deem immunity granted by treaty or other agreement to be waived. Waiver of immunity might result either from express agreement between the parties to a contract or by implied acquiescence of the party purporting to enjoy immunity through overt or covert acts. The leading case in this area concerns the 1967 decision of *Lutcher SA Celulose e Papel* v. *Inter-American Development Bank*[10] where the District of Columbia Circuit Court ruled that the Inter- American Development Bank did not enjoy immunity as any immunity given to the bank had been waived by the Bank by virtue of Article XI(3) of its Articles of Agreement with a Brazilian Corporation who was the other party to the action. An advance waiver, incorporated in a commercial agreement, even though it is calculated to apply only to a particular situation, cannot be deemed invalid and will be generally applicable according to the merits of the case. In *Standard Chartered Bank* v. *International Tin Council and others*[11] The Queen's Bench in England rejected the claim that an advance waiver is inapplicable to a dispute if it were meant specifically in the contract to apply to "a particular case", which was interpreted by the court as a particular transaction and not a whole dispute. A choice of forum clause in a specific agreement could also be interpreted as a waiver of immunity from suit that could be effectively performed in advance.

The question is whether an international Organization such as ICAO must wholly be at the mercy of a national court. The argument has been adduced that domestic courts should not have absolute jurisdiction or adjudicatory authority over international organizations since such exercise of authority might cause damage or adversely affect that organization's independence. The rationale of this

---

[9] 524 *NYS* 2d., 971.

[10] 382 *F2d.* 454.

[11] [1987] 1 *WLR* 641.

argument was accepted by the Quebec Superior Court in 2003 where, in an instance where a former employee of ICAO sued ICAO et al. for wrongful dismissal from his position at ICAO, the court recognized the need to grant immunities to international organizations so that they could sustain their independence and freedom. The court drew a parallel between freedom and independence of the Organization with the notion of immunity, recognizing that neither an international organization nor a State should be subject to the laws and conditions of the courts of another State. The Court acknowledged the bifurcation of immunity into absolute and functional immunity and concluded that ICAO has quasi-absolute immunity in this particular case. According to the Court, functional immunity would be conferred regarding acts performed by officials of ICAO in the course of their duties and within the scope of their employment.

The above notwithstanding, it must be noted that, in the particular case of the public key directory, ICAO is not merely an overseer of the maintenance and administration of the PKD but has other functions such as being the agent of the group of States who own the directory as well as being a party to possible contracts with a provider of services and technology aimed at running the directory. The status of ICAO would clearly be bifurcated into that of an international organization bestowed with immunity similar to that enjoyed by a sovereign State in its overall role in being responsible for the maintenance of the directory and, on the other hand to being an organization which is a legal person having the capacity to enter into legally enforceable contracts. From the above discussion it could well be subsumed that ICAO would enjoy jurisdictional immunity and immunity for any act perceived as a sovereign act performed by a foreign State. With regard to any local contract that ICAO may enter into, courts may consider restrictive immunity depending on the merits of the case. With regard to tortious liability, it is clear that courts would view with serious apprehension any claim to immunity, in the light of persuasive legislation in many common law and civil law jurisdictions to the effect that there is no immunity for proven tortious liability.

Chapter 9
Conclusion

Arguably, the most important consideration for ICAO in this important and contentious exercise is to realize that in the ultimate analysis, it is its own enemy. Much of the work involved over the triennium 2014–2016 lies with the Secretariat. Yet, there is hardly evidence that this is a collective exercise. There should be at least three bureaux of ICAO continuously involved in developing a global MBM scheme and they are the Air Transport Bureau (ATB), the Air Navigation Bureau (ANB) and the Legal Affairs and External Relations Bureau (LEB). In most if not all meetings conducted by ICAO, particularly at the Council level, LEB is not present. The limitations of LEB input is reflected in the three superficial and woefully inadequate paragraphs in the *Report of the Assessment of Market—Based Measures.*

As already mentioned, any final result of a global MBM scheme should be coercive, enforceable and within the philosophy and meaning of the Chicago Convention. Ironically, the Council, under the Convention, has only functions (which are in essence duties) and no powers.[1] On the other hand the Assembly has powers and duties accorded to it in the Chicago Convention,[2] one of which is to delegate to the Council the powers and authority necessary or desirable for the discharge of the duties of the Organization and revoke or modify the delegations of authority at any time.[3] However, in this instance there is no indication that the Assembly exercised its powers to delegate its authority or power to the Council. On the contrary Assembly Resolution A38-18 clearly States that it will be the Assembly that decides to develop a global MBM scheme for international aviation, taking into account the work of the Council.

---

[1] Although Jacob Schenkman, in his well documented and logically reasoned treatise on ICAO states that "The Council has been entrusted with duties, powers and functions..." he does not give a single example of such a power. See Capt. Jacob Schenkman, *International Civil Aviation Organization*, Librairie E. Droz: Geneve, 1955 at 158.

[2] Article 49 of the Convention.

[3] Article 49 h.

© The Author(s) 2014
R. Abeyratne, *Aviation and Climate Change*, SpringerBriefs in Law,
DOI: 10.1007/978-3-319-08443-5_9

It must be noted that ICAO can generally only work on the basis of legal powers that are attributed to it. Presumably, these powers emanate from the sovereign States that form the membership of such organizations (See de Witte 1998). Therefore, the logical conclusion is that if international organizations were to act beyond the powers accorded to them, they would be presumed to act ultra vires (Klabbers 2002). It should be noted that ICAO does not only derive implied authority from its Contracting States based on universality but it also has attribution from States to exercise certain powers. The doctrine of attribution of powers comes directly from the will of the founders, and in ICAO's case, powers were attributed to ICAO when it was established as an international technical organization and a permanent civil aviation agency to administer the provisions of the Chicago Convention. In addition, ICAO could lay claims to what are now called "inherent powers" which give ICAO power to perform all acts that the Organization needs to perform to attain its aims not due to any specific source of organizational power but simply because ICAO inheres in organization hood. Therefore, as long as acts are not prohibited in ICAO's constituent document (the Chicago Convention), they must be considered legally valid (Seyersted 1963).

Over the past 2 decades the inherent powers doctrine has been attributed to the United Nations Organization and its specialized agencies on the basis that such organizations could be stultified if they were to be bogged down in a quagmire of interpretation and judicial determination in the exercise of their duties. The advantages of the inherent powers doctrine is twofold. Firstly, inherent powers are functional and help the organization concerned to reach its aims without being tied by legal niceties. Secondly, it relieves the organization of legal controls that might otherwise effectively preclude that organization from achieving its aims and objectives. The ability to exercise its inherent powers has enabled ICAO to address issues on aviation insurance and establish an insurance mechanism; perform mandatory audits on States in the fields of aviation safety and security; and establish a funding mechanism to finance aviation safety projects, all of which are not provided for in the Chicago Convention but are not expressly prohibited.

With regard to the conferral of powers by States to ICAO, States have followed the classic approach of doing so through an international treaty. However, neither is there explicit mention of such a conferral on ICAO in the Chicago Convention nor is there any description of ICAO's powers, except for an exposition of ICAO's aims and objectives. The Council of ICAO is designated both mandatory and permissive "functions", although the Council could impose certain measures when provisions of the Convention are not followed. Therefore States have not followed the usual style of conferral of powers in the case of ICAO, which, along the lines of the decision of the International Court of Justice in the 1996 *WHO Advisory Opinion* case[4] was that the powers conferred on international organizations are normally the subject of express statement in their constituent instruments.[5] This

---

[4] *Legality of the Threat or Use of Nuclear Weapons, Advisory Opinion*, ICJ Reports, 1996, p. 64.
[5] Id. p. 79.

notwithstanding, it cannot be disputed that ICAO Contracting States have conferred certain powers on ICAO to perform its functions independently. For example, ICAO is a legal entity having the power to enter into legal agreements with legal entities including other international organizations with regard to the performance of its functions.

Conversely, an international organization must accept conferred powers on the basis of Article 34 of the Vienna Convention on the Law of Treaties which stipulates that a treaty does not create rights or obligations of a third State without its consent. This principle can be applied mutatis mutandis to an international organization such as ICAO. The conferral of powers on an international organization does not ipso facto curtail the powers of a State to act outside the purview of that organization unless a State has willingly limited its powers in that respect. This principle was recognized in the *Lotus* Case[6] where the Provisional International Court of Justice held that a State can exercise powers on a unilateral basis even while the conferral to the Organization remains in force. The Court held that restrictions upon the independence of States cannot be presumed.[7]

ICAO's conferred powers enable the Organization to adopt binding regulations by majority decision (which is usually unnecessary as most of ICAO policy is adopted through consensus). However, States could opt out of these policies or make reservations thereto, usually before such policy enters into force. This is because States have delegated power to ICAO to make decisions on the basis that they accept such decisions on the international plane. In such cases States could contract out and enter into binding agreements outside the purview of ICAO even on subjects on which ICAO has adopted policy. The only exception to this rule lies in the adoption of Standards in Annex 2 to the Chicago Convention on Rules of the Air, in particular navigation over the high seas and other over flight areas where freedom of flight prevails which all Contracting States are bound to follow in order to maintain global safety.

Leadership is the key to ICAO's role in the Twenty First Century, and nowhere is its need more pronounced than in the environmental field. The inhibitive mindset created by the Chicago Convention where Article 44 ascribes to ICAO only a watered down role to merely "foster the planning and development of international air transport" would militate against any cultural transformation that would demand a more greater leadership role from ICAO. The archaic and hopelessly obsolete premise that ICAO's aim should be "to meet the needs of the peoples of the world for safe, regular, efficient and economical air transport" is diametrically opposed to the new thinking in the ICAO leadership that, in a competitive world, ICAO has to perform 100 % in helping develop an air transport system that is sustainable and efficient.

ICAO's leadership role in the economic and technical fields of civil aviation hinges on two key factors: an aggressive operational plan structure with key

---

[6] *PCIJ Reports* Series A, No. 10, p. 4.

[7] Id. p. 18.

performance indicators and targets; and the realization that organizational culture, which is an intangible asset, is the new frontier of competitive advantage. The latter is particularly important under the current circumstances of ICAO where human resources and expertise are in short supply. Cultural transformation starts with the leadership and, their individual and leadership values. When one looks at Looking at ICAO's current leadership structure, there is no room for doubt that this is not in short supply. However the trick would be to motivate the staff sufficiently so that they would be impelled to follow their leaders in the transformation and forge ICAO's leadership forward in its various areas of work.

All this leads one to the bottom line, which is the need for a change in the mindset of the Organization, from its service role to a role of implementation and assistance. The human factor is an essential consideration in this metamorphosis. The key, however, and the starting point, however, is to recognize the need for the transition, which ICAO has already done. The next step is to recognize that ICAO needs its peoples' best efforts, both individually and collectively. ICAO's image and the perception of the outside world of ICAO as an effective Organization would be anchored on the extent to which its workers represent themselves as good stewards of ICAO's business. They should therefore work together in the overarching interest of the Organization. When all these factors are considered together, there is nothing to suggest that ICAO is headed in the wrong direction.

ICAO's overriding philosophy, in the context of the foregoing discussion should be based on two simple philosophical truths: the first is that sustainable development has three main considerations: economic development; social development; and environmental protection. The second is the philosophy based on principle 16 of the Rio Declaration on Environment and Development, which internalizes external factors and effects of emissions in the "polluter pays" principle to the effect that " National authorities should endeavour to promote the internalization of environmental costs and the use of economic instruments, taking into account the approach that the polluter should, in principle, bear the cost of pollution, with due regard to the public interest and without distorting international trade and investment". This brings to bear the inexorable fact that while the "polluter pays" principle is straightforward enough, what is most important is the phrase "without distorting international trade and investment".

This in turn resurfaces the Paretian concept that a global MBM should be introduced and implemented so that at least one party benefits while no party loses. In other words any imposition on aviation engine emissions should not go towards penalizing any one State in its overall trade potential.

So what is "distorting international trade and investment"? There are some questions that have to be initially addressed which may help avoid trade and investment distortion. Curiously, they are in the Chicago Convention itself. The Preamble to the Convention says inter alia, "...the undersigned governments having agreed on certain principles and arrangements in order that international civil aviation may be developed in a safe and orderly manner and that international air transport services may be established on the basis of equality of opportunity and operated soundly and economically". Here, one could immediately draw a link between "equality of opportunity" and the CBDR and SCRC concepts.

One way of looking at it is that distortion of international trade and investment would tantamount to distortion of competition. This makes sense, particularly from the point of view of the Chicago Convention as just mentioned. Air transport affects world trade in two ways: as a service by itself, directly transporting persons and freight; and as a service feeding other areas of trade mainly involving tourism and hospitality. However, it cannot be doubted that air transport affects overall economic activities of business, particularly involving cross-border trade. It is also incontrovertible that the world needs an efficient and effective air transport industry if the dual functions of the air transport service were to be sustained over time to cater to the rapidly growing demand for carriage by air of persons and goods. In order to achieve this objective, the air transport industry must be liberalized to the extent that it remains unfettered by commercial constraints. Yet, unlike most other modes of transport, air transport remains rather rigidly controlled by the need for agreements of States to permit carriers of other States into their territories as well as established percentages of national ownership of air carriers which stifle foreign investment in national jurisdictions. While at least one commentator has categorically stated that the trend towards a very liberal open skies international regime is unstoppable (Doganis 2001), which implicitly gives the industry the assurance that the problem would solve itself in the years to come, others have vigorously advocated that, as a panacea to the problem of rigid regulation, market access in air transport should be in the domain of a liberalized international regime. While the former view cannot be disputed, the latter approach brings to bear the compelling need to address the issue squarely, both in terms of whether the desirable approach would be to bring the industry from the current bilateral structure of air services negotiations into a more generalized regime and if so, what the modalities of such an exercise might entail. As to the former, it is largely a matter of political will. The latter would need some discussion on the legalities involved.

The ultimate issue could well be, does a global MBM adversely affect the right bestowed on any State by the Chicago Convention to compete in the air transport market so as to gain the full economic benefit for that State through such services. A points come to mind. It is important to note that the economic significance of the Chicago Convention lies entirely in its main theme—of meeting the needs of the peoples of the world for economical air transport, whilst preventing waste through unfair competition and providing for a fair opportunity for all States concerned to operate air services. In order to accomplish this goal, the Convention, through ICAO, has to consider all aspects of economic implications that the operation of international air services by commercial air transport enterprises of the world, particularly those of the member States of ICAO, pose.

In August 1945, at the first meeting of the Opening Session of the Interim Council of the Provisional International Civil Aviation Organization (PICAO), the Hon. C.D. Howe, Minister of Reconstruction, Canada said:

We (Canada) believe that there must be greater freedom for development of international air transport and that this freedom may best be obtained within a framework which provides equality of opportunity and rewards for efficiency.[8]

Dr. Edward Warner, Representative of the United States of America (later the first President of the ICAO Council) said at the same meeting:

Our first purpose will be to smooth the paths for civil flying wherever we are able. We shall seek to make it physically easier, safer, more reliable, more pleasant; but I believe it will be agreed also that we should maintain the constant goal that civil aviation should contribute to international harmony. The civil use of aircraft must so develop asto bring the peoples closer together, letting nation speak more understandingly unto nation.[9]

Dr. Warner had notably stressed on the purpose of civil aviation to be the promotion of international harmony and dialogue between nations. He had also made it clear that the seminal task of civil aviation is to bring the people of the world together through understanding and interaction. It is clear that at this stage at least, civil aviation was recognised more as a social necessity rather than a mere economic factor. In addition, through the statements of Minister Howe and Dr. Warner, one can glean the attitude of the international community towards aviation at that time:

- that civil aviation was based on equality of opportunity: and,
- that it was a social need rather than a fiscal tool.

The above notwithstanding, the American approach at the Conference to market access, particularly in terms of air traffic rights, is embodied in the statement of Adolf Berle, the Assistant Secretary at that time in the State Department when he said:

I feel that aviation will have a great influence on American foreign interests and American foreign policy than any other non-political consideration…it may well be determinative in certain territorial matters which have to do with American defence, as well as with transportation matters affecting American commerce, in a degree comparable to that which sea power has had on our interests and policy (Mackenzie 2010).

This certainly goes above and beyond using air transport as a social need on the basis of equality of opportunity.

The First Interim Assembly of the Provisional International Civil Aviation Organization (PICAO) was held in May 1946. This Session set the scene for identifying issues that had culminated in the provisions of the Chicago Convention. In the period that followed the First Interim Assembly Session, PICAO commissioned a group of experts called Commission 3 to draft a multilateral agreement on commercial rights for aircraft, which culminated in a Draft Multilateral Agreement on Commercial Rights. The Draft Agreement contained three basic elements:

---

[8] *PICAO Documents*, Montreal, 1945, Volume 1, Doc 1, at 3.

[9] Id. Doc 2, at 2.

- a grant of the right to operate commercially to a reasonable number of traffic centres serving as conveniently as is practicable each State's international traffic;
- a basic regulatory provision dealing with the amount of capacity to be provided, with subsidiary provisions designed to prevent abuses; and,
- a provision for the settlement of differences between Contracting States through arbitral tribunals with power to render binding decisions.[10]

The only provisions of the draft on which unanimous agreement was not reached were those concerning routes and airports and capacity. Commission 3 also inquired into the distinction between scheduled and non-scheduled services as they appeared in Articles 5 and 6 of the Chicago Convention.

As a result of the study of Commission 3 on scheduled and non-scheduled air transport, the Air Transport Committee, at the 17th Session of the ICAO Council, examined in 1952, a Secretariat study on regulations in international non-scheduled aviation. The study found that at the time, national policies with respect to the taking on or discharging of traffic in their territories by foreign non-scheduled aircraft had taken a variety of forms. There were 13 States which required prior permission for each individual flight or series of flights where the granting of permission was based on the circumstances of each case. 10 States required that permission for non-scheduled flights should be granted for each flight or series of flights subject to prescribed regulations. Some States required specific bilateral agreements, while others demanded reciprocal treatment for their carriers.[11] Five European States were known to have made arrangements by means of formal bilateral arrangements for the regulation of non-scheduled commercial flights between their territories.[12]

The Committee also noted that the Council had expressed the view that a "stop for non-traffic purposes" as referred to in Article 5 of the Convention should be taken to include the freedom to load and unload passengers or goods not carried for remuneration or hire. The Council had also considered "remuneration or hire" to mean something received for the act of transportation from someone other than the operator. This interpretation would mean that flights carried out on the business of the operator would receive the freedom granted by the first paragraph of Article 5.[13] The Council's analysis of Article 5 also indicated that the State flown over must not consider its right to require landing as a matter of course and that this right, as granted in the provision, must not be exercised too restrictively. Consideration was also given to the fact that although the Chicago Convention, by Article 3, precludes its application to State aircraft, most States may be prepared to agree that civilian State aircraft should be given the type off free passage described in the first

---

[10] *Views of Commission No 3, Doc 4023*, A-1 - P/3, 1/4/47. See also *C-WP/369*, 22/6/49 for a detailed discussion on the Commission's work on the Agreement.

[11] *AT-WP/295, 15 Dec 52* at 5.

[12] Ibid.

[13] See *AT-WP/296*, 15/12/52, at 9.

paragraph of Article 5.[14] The same right may be given to emergency operations, taxi type flights and all inclusive charter tours.[15]

An analysis containing the above views of the ICAO Council, together with a definitive report by Council to Contracting States of scheduled international air services[16] as referred to in Article 6 of the Chicago Convention was adopted by Council at its Fifteenth Session on 28 March 1952. This Report contained the fact that a scheduled international air service must in the first instance consist of a series of flights. A single flight by itself could thus not constitute a scheduled international air service. Article 6 therefore requires that a series of flights must be performed through the air space over the territory of more than one State and performed by aircraft for the transport of passengers, cargo or mail for remuneration in order to constitute a scheduled national air service. The service must be performed so as to serve traffic between the same two or more points, either according to a published time table, or with flights so regular or frequent that they constitute a recognizably systematic series.[17] The word "remuneration" in the provision has the same application and meaning as in Article 5.

Finally, the most important factor for consideration—international law. ICAO is governed not only by the Chicago Convention but by the United Nations Charter. Article 55 of the Charter provides that, with a view to the creation of conditions of stability and well-being which are necessary for peaceful and friendly relations among nations based on respect for the principle of equal rights and self-determination of peoples, the United Nations shall promote: higher standards of living, full employment, and conditions of economic and social progress and development; solutions of international economic, social, health, and related problems; and international cultural and educational cooperation; and universal respect for, and observance of, human rights and fundamental freedoms for all without distinction as to race, sex, language, or religion. Article 56 goes on to say: "All Members pledge themselves to take joint and separate action in cooperation with the Organization for the achievement of the purposes set forth in Article 55.

Under this umbrella, what must be remembered is that a multilateral environmental agreement (MEA) which imposes a global MBM on the aviation community would not be the result of simplistic or peripheral aviation concerns and interests alone. The causative and influential factors could be multifarious. As one commentator says:

---

[14] Ibid.

[15] AT-WP/296 *supra*, note 180 at 10.

[16] The ICAO Assembly, at its Second Session held in Geneva in June 1948, adopted Resolution A2-18 which called for the adoption by Council of a definition of the term "scheduled international air service. See Doc 7670, *supra*, note 82, at 79–80.

[17] See, *Report By the Council to Contracting States on the Definition of a Scheduled International Air Service and the Analysis of the Rights Conferred by Article 5 of the Convention. Doc 7278, C/841, 10/5/52.*

Much of international environmental law today is preoccupied with regional or global concerns of various kinds, rather than with bilateral concerns over transboundary pollution. Solutions to regional and global environmental problems require broad-based cooperation, often in situations of uncertainty as to causes and ultimate effects of a given type of pollution or degradation. Moreover, pollution and environmental decline typically do not result from state conduct per se, but from activities within states. This means that solutions for many environmental problems require fundamental adjustments to social and economic patterns. It also means that... the root causes both of environmental problems and of failures to combat them, are often not lack of respect for international standards, but gaps in economic, regulatory and technical capacity.[18]

Sustainable development is after all, economic development; social development; and environmental protection all rolled into one.

References

de Witte B (1998) Sovereignty and European integration: the weight of tradition. In: Slaughter A-M et al (eds) The European court and national courts: doctrine and jurisprudence. Hart Publishing, Oxford, pp 277–304

Doganis R (2001) The airline business in the 21st century. Routeledge, London, p 11

Klabbers J (2002) An introduction to international institutional law. Cambridge University Press, Cambridge 60

Mackenzie D (2010) ICAO—a history of the international civil aviation organization. University of Toronto Press, Toronto, p 3

Seyersted F (1963) Objective international personality of intergovernmental organizations: do their capacities really depend upon the conventions establishing them?. Finn Seyersted Publisher, Copenhagen, p 28

---

[18]   Jutta Brunee, *supra*, note 289, at 9.